PAUL GREEN'S

PLANT
BOOK

ELDERBERRY IN FLOWER

PAUL GREEN'S

PLANT BOOK

An Alphabet of Flowers & Folklore

EDITED BY
BETSY GREEN MOYER
& KEN MOORE

PHOTOGRAPHY BY
BETSY GREEN MOYER
& BYRD GREEN CORNWELL

Book Design by Dorrit Green

BOTANICAL GARDEN
FOUNDATION, INC.

© 2005 Betsy Green Moyer

Published by the Botanical Garden Foundation, Inc. ,
of the North Carolina Botanical Garden

Proceeds from the sale of the Plant Book *will support the
North Carolina Botanical Garden's Education Program.*

Moyer, Betsy Green
Paul Green's Plant Book: An Alphabet of Flowers and Folklore
Betsy Green Moyer and Ken Moore, editors
Includes references and index

ISBN 1-889065-01-3 (Hard cover)
ISBN 1-889065-02-1 (Soft cover)

1. Paul Green. 2. Wildflowers—North Carolina. 3. Photography—wildflowers.
4. Folklore—North Carolina. 5. Medicine—herbal.

To my parents,
Paul and Elizabeth Green,
who never forgot to smell the flowers
and whose love for all living things
inspired the creation of this book.

—Betsy Green Moyer

CONTENTS

PHOTO: MEADOW RUE FLOWERS

BEECH TREES AT FOREST THEATER, CHAPEL HILL, LOCATION OF 1917 PRODUCTION OF PAUL GREEN'S FIRST PLAY

ABOUT PAUL GREEN

(1894-1981)

PAUL GREEN GREW UP on a cotton farm in rural Harnett County, North Carolina. He learned the value of hard physical labor as well as the importance and beauty of literature and music. He read books in the fields as he followed a mule-drawn plow.

By teaching school he earned enough money to enter the University of North Carolina, Chapel Hill, but his college education was interrupted by World War I. After returning to the University he continued his education, focusing on drama and philosophy, both of which he taught at UNC-Chapel Hill after his graduation.

Paul Green's total literary output included not only outdoor plays and dramas, for which he won a 1927 Pulitzer Prize, but also novels, essays, cinema scripts, and poetry. His last work, published posthumously in 1990, was his beloved *Wordbook: An Alphabet of Reminiscence,* the result of a lifetime of collecting words, expressions, proverbs, games, herbal remedies, botanical information, and stories of the folk. During his long lifetime he never strayed far from his people nor far from his roots.

PAUL GREEN AT WINDY OAKS FARM, THE GREENS' HOME NEAR CHAPEL HILL FROM 1963

The Paul Green cabin at the North Carolina Botanical Garden, Chapel Hill

ABOUT THE NORTH CAROLINA BOTANICAL GARDEN

by Peter White, Director

ABOUT 1990, Rhoda Wynn and Sally Vilas, two friends of the North Carolina Botanical Garden, came to visit me at the Garden to ask whether the Garden would consider being the new home of the log cabin once used by Paul Green, a much loved and respected playwright who was also a professor of drama at the University of North Carolina at Chapel Hill. I had come to the University and the North Carolina Botanical Garden long after Paul Green's career, but I already knew what a charismatic and interesting figure he was. His legacy was much in evidence in Chapel Hill and through the plays that were still being produced and which captured some of the history of North Carolina.

I soon found myself visiting a very rundown old cabin about two miles away from the Garden. It had spirit, but how would we move it and how would it be restored? I was new to the Garden and new to the idea of fund raising. The Garden hadn't had a great deal of experience in that area anyway. Somehow, though, we convinced ourselves it could be done and somehow our friends convinced the University to think of the legacy and the potential (rather than the condition of the cabin itself). The budget seemed like a huge sum, more than we had any experience raising. But the fans of Paul Green started pitching in, problems of ownership and insurance were sorted out, and there it was: the cabin coming down the highway, surrounded by police cars, on a wide flatbed truck!

We owe something else to this project: it was the first daring, expensive, and important project that the Garden undertook to redevelop its site. And from this project we learned it could be done. From there we gained confidence and have gone on to raise many times the cost of that first project. Moving and restoring the Paul Green Cabin, though, got us started on a series of improvements that have been remaking the Garden ever since.

The Garden wanted the Paul Green Cabin for two reasons. First, it shows that artists take inspiration from nature, for Paul Green would escape the campus to write in this cabin. He cared a great deal about the cabin and there are wonderful pictures of him relaxing and working there. Second, Paul Green was interested in the relationship of all southern people and their landscapes. His interest in southern culture included understanding the botany and plants of the southeast, including the plants that those peoples used. He wrote about a time when people were closer to the land and closer to the plants and animals with which they shared their fields, gardens, and woods. The Paul Green Cabin therefore became a natural focus for the interpretation of the field of ethnobotany (the relationship of plants and cultures).

As a botanist I have a prejudice: the best writers are always good botanists. I would be happy to reel off the botanical details in Shakespeare, Yeats, Blake, Frost, and others. I am delighted to add Paul Green to this list. Now, why do I believe good writers are also botanists? Being a botanist demands the same attention to detail and the same powers of observation that writing demands. That's my theory, anyway.

This book presents the botany of Paul Green in a beautiful and accessible way, and the Garden is thrilled to help bring it to you.

THE CATTAIL GATE, ENTRANCE TO THE NORTH CAROLINA BOTANICAL GARDEN, CHAPEL HILL

TRAILING ARBUTUS AT BARBECUE CHURCH NEAR LILLINGTON, NORTH CAROLINA

INTRODUCTION

by Ken Moore, Assistant Director 1986-2003,
North Carolina Botanical Garden

PAUL GREEN WAS A PASSIONATE RECORDER of the heritage of all the folks living in his homeland, the "Valley," his affectionate term for the Cape Fear River Basin. Following in his footsteps many years later is his daughter, Betsy Green Moyer, who is equally passionate in combining her photography talents with her reverence for her dad's stories and keen observations. In 2002 Betsy set upon an ambitious project to extract the botanical references from *Paul Green's Wordbook: An Alphabet of Reminiscence,* to photograph many of those plants, and to "do a book" to be called *Paul Green's Plant Book: An Alphabet of Flowers and Folklore.* Incredibly, in less than three years, here you have it, an engaging edition of Paul Green's plant observations and plant-related stories accompanied throughout with beautiful color images of many of those plants.

Acknowledging that she was not well versed in plant identification and also determined to photograph her dad's referenced plants in the environs of his Valley, Betsy contacted the North Carolina Botanical Garden seeking a botanist to assist her. In response to that call I thought it most appropriate to have such a project associated with the Botanical Garden, which is now the home of the Paul Green Cabin, the daily creative retreat that Paul Green moved piece by piece and reconstructed near his Chapel Hill home, Greenwood, so many decades earlier. I was happy to lead Betsy to the many plants she wished to photograph, but little did I realize what a botanical adventure was about to unfold on what I considered familiar turf.

New Discoveries. The surprising challenges and frustrations that evolved during this endeavor were far overshadowed by first-time observations of obscure and seldom

SUGARBERRY FLOWERS, DETAIL

noticed flowers of otherwise common plants, as well
as finding some of the very plants described by Paul
Green still on their original sites. The tiny flower of
the snakeroot or pelican flower (see page 61) was a new
sighting for me, and each time I view that image my
consciousness returns to the thrill of that first observation. And the magic of noticing for the first time
the tiny flowers of the hackberry or sugarberry tree
(see opposite) will remain forever fresh.

BETSY MOYER PHOTOGRAPHING PYXIE PLANT,
SPOUT SPRINGS, NORTH CAROLINA

Each time Betsy traveled down to North Carolina
from her home in Massachusetts we made excursions
down to the Valley because she wished to photograph
the plants in the vicinity of her dad's observations.
Each of these excursions provided special discoveries
for us both. One such discovery was finding trailing
arbutus hanging onto a steep embankment just above the old spring behind Barbecue
Church near Paul Green's home place at Lillington. His description of the annual
early spring pilgrimage with his wife, Elizabeth, to find that sweet-scented wildflower
above the spring behind the church, where Flora MacDonald and her husband
worshipped during those couple of years in the 1770's when they resided in the Valley,
was captivating, indeed. Needless to say, Betsy and I shouted with joy on that very
same wooded slope when we discovered the trailing arbutus, still there and in flower,
where her dad and mom observed it so many decades earlier and where Flora
MacDonald may have noticed it two centuries before!

Another really special moment was rediscovering the rare little pixie flower or
pyxie moss on a sandy flat near Spout Springs, N.C., where Dr. B.W. Wells discovered
and described it back in the early 1930's. The plants at this site of the original discovery,
called the "type habitat," were believed to have been eradicated by construction activi-
ty years ago, so finding several mats of thriving plants was indeed a joyful rediscovery.
Efforts are now being made to secure the pyxie moss site for permanent preservation.

The Challenge of Common Names. Entering Paul Green's folk heritage world of
the Valley, which included so many localized common plant names, provided for me
numerous unanticipated challenges and frustrations. My many years of interpreting
native plants for the general public had accustomed me to many instances of a single
plant having two or three common names. Little prepared was I for the multiplicity
of common names described in the *Plantbook*. In those entries where Paul Green

actually described the plants from his own observations, the botanical identification was relatively easy. When he did not record visual descriptions and there were multiple common names, determining what plant was the target of our search for Betsy's artistic camera eye was definitely a challenge.

What does one do when a common name like snakeroot is connected to at least three or more separate plant families? Another example is the common name, wintergreen, which when matched with Paul Green's descriptions clearly refers to three different genera and species: *Gaultheria procumbens* (commonly known as wintergreen), *Chimaphala maculata* (commonly known as pipsissewa) and *Mitchella repens* (commonly known as partridgeberry). They all are low to the ground evergreen plants, so one can easily understand how local folks throughout a large region may apply one name to different plants.

Well, what I consider "common name frustration" is also the charm and fascination of folk heritage. Thankfully I had the 1958 publication *Index of Plants of North Carolina with Reputed Medicinal Uses* by Marion Lee Jacobs and Henry M. Burlage as a guide in matching numerous common names to specific botanical Latin names. And apparently Paul Green was also guided by Henry Burlage, as he made reference more than once to "my friend Burlage," in various descriptions.

In *Paul Green's Plant Book: An Alphabet of Flowers and Folklore,* to reflect the rich

heritage of the folks of his homeland, we are remaining faithful to the common names and spellings recorded by Paul Green, even when those names are not commonly recognized in present day.

Botanical Names. For the official botanical name, the Latin name, for each plant described, our official reference is *The Manual of the Vascular Flora of the Carolinas* by Albert E. Radford, Harry E. Ahles and C. Ritchie Bell. This taxonomic work produced in 1968 has for decades been the "green Bible" of native plant identification for the Southeast. *The Flora of the Carolinas, Virginia, and Georgia, A Working Draft of March 17, 2004,* by Alan S. Weakley, was consulted frequently for

SASSAFRAS FLOWERS

verifications and descriptions. It is acknowledged that this latest taxonomic authority makes numerous changes in the botanical nomenclature, based on current scientific research, but since this revised authority is still a work-in-progress, the decision was made to adhere to the more familiar nomenclature of the "green Bible," for simplicity. In addition, the most recently published *Second Edition of Wild Flowers of North Carolina,* by William S. Justice, C. Ritchie Bell and Anne H. Lindsey, a very beautiful and user-friendly identification guide to the flora of the Southeast, was used as an invaluable resource.

This is Not an Identification Guide. *Paul Green's Plant Book: An Alphabet of Flowers and Folklore* is not an identification guide to the plants of the region. For more complete information you are directed to the identification guides described above and listed under *Further Reading* on page 117.

KEN MOORE AND BETSY MOYER
PREPARE FOR A PHOTOGRAPHIC FIELD TRIP

This book is a visual foray into the botanical and horticultural heritage of *Paul Green's Wordbook.* Though many of the plant images are typical of the subject, some are of seldom-observed seasonal stages of the plants, such as the persimmon (page 44) and pawpaw (page 42) in flower. Most folks are familiar with the three types of leaves borne by the sassafras tree, but how many amongst us are familiar with the sassafras flowers that emerge in early spring before the leaves? Many of the images are flower details of aspects that intrigued Betsy and me as we searched for various plants through the seasons. Hopefully, some of the images are surprises to you and all will bring you pleasure. And for each of you, I hope that the emphasis on the plant heritage here in *Paul Green's Plant Book: An Alphabet of Flowers and Folklore* will entice you to go to the original two-volume collection, *Paul Green's Wordbook: An Alphabet of Reminiscence,* on a pleasurable journey to experience more fully the rich human and environmental heritage that is a part of our region.

PREFACE

by Betsy Green Moyer

T HIS BOOK BRINGS TOGETHER my passion for wildlife photography and my father Paul Green's writings from the last and one of my favorite of his books, *Paul Green's Wordbook: An Alphabet of Reminiscence.*

At his death in 1981, his beloved *Wordbook* was an unfinished project. Rhoda Wynn, his loyal assistant of fourteen years, edited the manuscript and in 1990 oversaw its publication. The two volumes, containing 1241 pages of words, proverbs, anecdotes, folk remedies, games, expressions, superstitions, ballads, and stories, collected during most of his adult life, is a veritable lexicon of Southern folklore, more

SWEET GUM, FALL FOLIAGE

specifically of the Cape Fear Valley in North Carolina where he grew up.

Among the entries are several hundred referring specifically to plants, shrubs, and trees native to North Carolina. I hoped to cull from the *Wordbook* those entries referring to native flora and to publish a separate book illustrated with my own photographs, similar to the displays on the walls of the Paul Green Cabin on the grounds of the North Carolina Botanical Garden.

Ken Moore, recently retired Assistant Director of the Garden, agreed to work with me, to provide the taxonomy and botanical notes, and to guide me through the terrain of North Carolina in search of wildflowers.

I have adhered as faithfully as possible to the text of the original *Wordbook* but have rearranged the sentences so that the entries generally follow a common format, beginning with Paul Green's botanical descriptions, followed by folk remedies or usages. His personal reminiscences are in italics. (In the case of double entries, for example, arbutus and trailing arbutus, I have combined the texts under one entry, in this case under "trailing arbutus.")

About the photos: Many were taken at the North Carolina Botanical Garden in Chapel Hill, during ten photographic expeditions to the Cape Fear Valley, home to my father for most of his life. Some images are close-ups of a particular aspect of a plant, tree, or shrub, usually the flower. Some show the full plant; others a clump or field.

The names of plants are Paul Green's. In some cases these are not the names by which the plants are most commonly known today. However, out of respect for his personal experience and knowledge, I have used his entry designations. (For example, twin bluebells are more commonly known as wild petunias.) Punctuation marks, commas, apostrophes, etc., generally have been left as is, since their presence—or absence—contributes to the flow and the colloquial quality of his narrative.

The reader should note that he or she assumes complete responsibility
for any ill effects that may be experienced by trying some of the remedies
and concoctions mentioned in the Plant Book.

Dogwoods blooming at Greenwood, the Greens' home outside Chapel Hill, 1936-1963

PAUL GREEN'S
PLANT BOOK

The Valley referred to in this collection is the area bordering the Cape Fear River, which originates in Chatham County, near Chapel Hill, North Carolina, and ends close to Wilmington on the Atlantic coast. The river flows through Harnett County, between Buie's Creek and Lillington, where Paul Green was born and spent his childhood. 🐌

ADAM AND EVE *Aplectrum hyemale*

A curious little flower belonging to the orchid family. Its two bulbs just below the ground are joined together—"Adam and Eve hand in hand." Later the two other bulbs, "Cain and Abel," appear, a close family group. Inside the bulbs is a strong glutinous matter from which the plant is sometimes referred to as putty root. When this root is chewed or brewed, it is supposed to be good for throat or bronchial trouble.

ADDER'S-TONGUE[1] *Erythronium americanum*

More commonly known as dogtooth violet, this popular southern flower is often called trout flower or trout lily. It was once used as a medicinal herb, the juice to bathe severe eye inflammations and the leaves, applied to wounds and placed gently over chilblains, were therapeutic. Like the sunflower, the adder's-tongue turns its little devoted head to follow its lord the sun and, like the rue anemone, too, it is a perfect flower to tramp the woods for in one's springtime courting days.

🐌 *So did I, so did she.*

ADDER'S-TONGUE

AGUE WEED *Gentiana quinquefolia*

The stiff gentian, also called gall weed. In the old days tea made from it was used as a tonic to purify the blood and to help in female disorders.

ALDER *Alnus serrulata*

A shrub, also called elder or tag alder, that grows plentifully along streams and in swamps in the Valley. A gargle made from the bark was supposed to cure sore throat, and it was also used for an emetic as well as for tanning and dyeing. Local baseball pitchers chewed it in the place of slippery elm to help them throw spit balls.

🪶 *In the old days we boys chewed the bark and spat out its red juice profusely, pretending that we were chewing tobacco.*

ALDER, FEMALE CONES

ALUMROOT[2] *Geranium maculatum*

Spotted geranium or wild geranium. It is common in the Valley and was used medically by the Indians and early settlers. A drink made from boiling the roots and leaves was supposed to be good for dysentery and diarrhea. Some old folks also used to say it was good for sore throat and ulcerations of the mouth, as well as general stomach disorders.

AMARANTH *Amaranthus spinosus*

Thorny amaranth, prickly careless-weed, and referred to sometimes as pigweed. It is widely scattered in the Valley and elsewhere in the South and grows as well in waste places as it does in the garden. There are several species of it which spread mat-like over the ground. It is easy to destroy if one gets at it early with his hoe, and like crabgrass, Johnson grass and nut grass was a curse to the Valley farmer. Like cabbage leaves, Jimson leaves and leaves of the

ALUMROOT

2 See *Botanical Notes*, pg. 113

mullein, the amaranth leaves were used to heal bites, wounds and all sorts of hurts, including nail-punctured feet.

APPLE OF PERU *Nicandra physalodes*
Peruvian bluebell. This plant is common in the wastelands of North Carolina. It was once used as a diuretic. Also used as a fly poison.

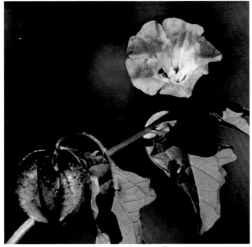

APPLE OF PERU, FLOWER AND POD

ARROWHEAD *Sagittaria latifolia*
A plant of the water plantain family found plentifully along the Valley streams and in swampy places and becoming more and more a favorite decorating and aerating feature in lily ponds.

ARTICHOKE *Helianthus tuberosus*
The kind we grew were called Jerusalem artichokes, also earth apples. A popular watery tuber, much used in the Valley for pickles. The tubers are edible, nutritious and were much prized by the Indians who enjoyed them as a succulent food.

ARTICHOKE

🐌 *My mother used to make artichoke pickles and for me they were a total watery loss. But many people like them. Dr. H.R. Totten of the Botany Department at the University of North Carolina once brought us a handful of tubers, and now looking out the window across the garden I can see plants flourishing seven feet tall. The rich ground there is alive with tasteless tubers.*

ARUM LEAF

ARUM *Peltandra virginica*
Often called wild calla or water-arum.
A swamp and stream plant, associate of arrow-
heads, pipeworts, yellow-eyed grasses and other
acid soil aquatics and becoming a feature of lily
ponds.
*It is a beautiful addition in our lily pool
in the summer and is said to be poisonous.
We have never tried to find out.*

BLUE ASTER

ASTER GRANDIFLORUS

ASTER *Aster spp.*
There are many species of this wild weed or
flower. The pastures and wastelands and roadsides are beautified in autumn by its profusion
of white, pink, blue, lavender and purple
bloomings.
*For all its beauty it still awaits the praise of
a single Valley poet.*

WILD AZALEA

AZALEA *Rhododendron nudiflorum*

Wild azalea, wild honeysuckle, or swamp pink.
A very popular shrub, and becoming more popular as the years go by. I would guess that at least
half the homes in the Valley now have this beautiful plant, both white and pink, somewhere on
their premises. Many azalea gardens have
become showplaces, for instance, those at
Wilmington or at Orton Plantation nearby.
Azalea festivals also are becoming popular.

🐚 *We children used to go into the woods in the
late springtime and gather the sticky sweet-
smelling flowers of the wild azalea by the armful
and bring them home to decorate the house.*

BAYBERRY *Myrica cerifera*

A wax-producing shrub, also referred to as
candleberry, waxberry or wax myrtle. The plant

BAYBERRY

has aromatic leaves and hard nut-like berries
coated with wax. Bayberry candles used to be
popular, made by pouring the melted wax of
the berries into wooden molds.

■ *A bayberry candle burned to the socket
Brings luck to the house and money to the pocket.*

LOVERS' CARVINGS ON THE BARK OF A BEECH TREE

BED STRAW

BED STRAW *Galium aparine*

Clabber grass. A fast growing creeper that will cover a garden plot in a few days if not gathered up. It is easily disposed of. Chewing it and swallowing the juice was supposed to be good for a nervous condition.

BEE BALM *Monarda didyma*

Also known as lemon balm, sweet balm, sweet Mary and sometimes called Oswego tea. A favorite aromatic plant, a member of the mint family. It grows luxuriantly in wet places and along stream banks from Maine to Florida. In the old days a tea made from it was good for fevers and to help women over their "monthlies."

BEECH *Fagus grandifolia*

This lovely tree is most common in the center and upper reaches of the Valley and is a favorite for lovers to carve their initials on. There is a common belief that it, like the sweet gum, is never struck by lightning. The bark was often used for tanning when red oak bark was not available.

BEGGAR LICE *Desmodium nudiflorum*

A pestering plant to anyone walking in wastelands or grown-over fields in late August or
September. A tea made from boiling the seed
was said to be an aid in easing the discomfort
of women's menstrual periods.

NATURE'S DOINGS

The lice or ticks, seeds of the beggar lice, stick to your trousers or dress most tenaciously. "So do they distribute themselves in the land," said my friend Dr. H. R. Totten at Chapel Hill. This caused me to ask if maybe they had a mind of their own and knew what they were doing.

His answer was a shrug and half a nod. There is much to ponder here, of course, as everywhere, as to nature's doings, and I have done a lot of that as I walked among the weeds, the woods, the flowers and other growing things in the Valley—not only with a shrug and half nod, but with a humbling of the head. "Do these all," I ask myself, "have the power to think?" As Dr. Totten might—and my old philosopher friend Mr. Mac would say, "Could be."

ABOVE: BEGGAR LICE FLOWERS AND SEEDS

BERMUDA GRASS *Cynodon dactylon*

Ant rice, Bahama grass, or wire grass. A farmer's
tough pest once it gets started but fine for heal-
ing up eroded places in land. This grass was
used widely as a purge when chewed. Even the
dogs still chew it to make themselves vomit.

BE-SHAME BUSH

BE-SHAME BUSH[3] *Schrankia microphylla*

The sensitive plant.

🐚 *We boys were taught that if you touched it
and said, "Be shame, be shame," the little leaflets
would close up. We soon saw they would close to
the touch with or without the words. We were also
told that if it thundered, the leaflets would close in
preparation for rain. I don't remember I ever
checked this out.*

[3] See *Botanical Notes*, pg. 113   7

BLACKBERRY *Rubus spp.*

A popular briary bush. Blackberry root tea was especially good for dysentery.

🐚 *We used to go blackberry picking and bring home bucketsful of the dark berries to be canned, made into jam or eaten fresh with sugar and milk.*

■ *Blackberry winter: A cold time that is supposed to come in May when the blackberry bushes are in blossom.*

BLACKBERRY FLOWERS

BEE GUM

This is a hollow gum for keeping bees, usually from a black gum tree. Also an old-timey container made by sawing off the length of a hollow tree and closing up one end of it for holding grain or other farm produce.

In the old days hunters kept their eyes out to find bee-trees. These were trees, usually hollow black gums, in which bees had built, and sometimes when they were cut down a great deal of honey could be got. I remember one man in Cumberland County telling me that he had cut down a bee-tree once and had over two hundred pounds of honey from it.

BLACK GUM *Nyssa sylvatica*

Toothbrush tree, often pronounced bla'gum. A tree that grows plentifully in swamps and lowlands. The wood is so tough that lumbermen leave it alone. The old trees often become hollow as they decay and die and bee gums were made from them. The little limb sprouts from the small trees made good toothbrushes—nearly all the snuff-dippers used them.

🐚 *We used to cut down a good-sized tree and saw off narrow sections to make wheels for our play wagons.*

BLACKBERRIES

BLACK HAW *Viburnum prunifolium*
A small tree or shrub that grows well in either damp or dry woods, common in the Valley as throughout the southeast. Tea made from the berries of this shrub was used, especially by the Negroes, as a blood purifier. The old grannies used it also to help prevent miscarriage.

BLACK JACK OAK

BLACK JACK *Quercus marilandica*
A tough slow-growing oak tree common to the sandhill country in the Valley. Pretty much worthless.

BLOODROOT *Sanguinaria canadensis*
This spring flower with its pale-lobed leaf and showy white blossoms grows in rich open woods from March into May. A tea made from the root is supposed, like carrots, to be good for the eyesight, also good for the nerves and coughs and colds. Two ounces of this tea in one pint of alcohol made a fine stimulant for both babies and rheumatic old men.

❧ *The babies were allowed two teaspoonfuls for a dose once a day. The old men could suit themselves. In the latter case I doubt the pint lasted very long.*

TOP: BLOODROOT IN FLOWER *BOTTOM:* BLOODROOT BUDS

9

BLUE CURLS

BLUE CURLS *Trichostema dichotomum*
An attractive flower usually found in dry open clearings from August to October. A tea made from the leaves and flowers was used as a gargle for sore throat and for diarrhea.

BONESET *Eupatorium perfoliatum*
A plant common to pastures and wasteland. It is also known as sweating plant. In late August and September its white flowers can be seen all along the roadside. A tea from its leaves or roots made a fine tonic and it was good for all kinds of diseases, including urinary troubles and female disorders. It was said that in the old, old days the doctors made bandages of the crushed leaves and wrapped them around a broken leg or arm to help it heal better, whence the name.

BROOM SAGE *Andropogon virginicus*
Broom sedge or broomstraw.
❧ *How often have we children been sent to the broomstraw patch to cut straw for making brooms. These we usually put together with a stick in the middle about halfway down and wrapped around with a rawhide string. They*

LEFT: BONESET.   *RIGHT:* FIELD OF BROOM SAGE AT MASON FARM BIOLOGICAL RESERVE, NORTH CAROLINA BOTANICAL.

LEFT: PAINTED BUCKEYE *RIGHT:* BUCKEYE NUTS

made wonderful brooms for sweeping the hearth but were very dangerous before the open fire. Many a child crawling along the floor got a broom into the fire and was badly burnt by it. My brother Hugh had a scarred wrist all his life from being burned so as a crawling baby.

BUCKEYE *Aesculus sylvatica*

Usually a shrub. A decoction from the bark was used in the old days for ulcers and toothache. I have never seen it large enough to be called a tree. But Messrs. Coker and Totten of the University of North Carolina reported that they found a buckeye in South Carolina 20 feet high and its body 3 1/2 inches in diameter, large enough to be called a tree. A buckeye nut or kernel was often carried in the pocket as a good luck charm.

🦢 *As a boy I carried one for several months but after a spell of what I thought was bad luck I threw it away. Mr. Mac said that his mother used buckeyes as a source of starch for clothes. He had heard from old folks too, he said, that the Indians would pound the kernels into a meal, mix it with beaten corn and water and throw the mush into rivers and creeks. The fish would eat it and get drunk on it and rise to the top and then were easy to catch as they floated on the water.*

BUTTERCUPS NEAR WINDY OAKS FARM, THE GREENS' HOME NEAR CHAPEL HILL

BUTTERCUP FLOWER

BUTTERCUP *Ranunculus acris*

There are several varieties of this lovely flower and all give a cheerful spring welcome with their yellow blossoms. The buttercup grows in meadows and pasturelands everywhere, and its bulbs, if eaten, result in stomach upheavals and heart pressures, so the old folks said.

BUTTERFLY WEED *Asclepias tuberosa*

A rather shy plant that grows rarely more than two feet tall here and there in dry soil. Its orange blossoms are especially attractive to butterflies. It was said to be good for the pleurisy and was often called pleurisy root. The Indians were said to have used it for a purgative and as a sweat-producer.

🍂 *My old Negro friend, Uncle Jerry McLean, told me that chewing its root and swallowing the juice was the best medicine "a-tall for snakebite."*

CATALPA *Catalpa speciosa*
Smoke inhaled from the parched and powdered catalpa leaves, like Jimson leaves, was a good asthma treatment. Also the multitude of worms that feed on the green leaves make good fish bait.

🍂 *The other day I saw an ad in the local paper— "Catalpa worms for sale, twenty-five cents a dozen."*

CATBRIER: *SMILAX ROTUNDIFOLIA* IN FLOWER

CATBRIER *Smilax spp.*
Carbriar. A specially clawing and cantankerous kind of brier. In the swamps and woods of the South it is also called a bramble.

BUTTERFLY WEED

CATTAILS

CATTAIL *Typha latifolia*

A common marsh or aquatic plant. Becoming very popular in the lily pools which the better-to-do folks in the Valley of recent years have been building.

CHERRY *Prunus serotina*

Next to the pine, the wild cherry is perhaps the most valuable of all medicinal plants and trees in the Valley. A tea made from cherry bark, especially from wild cherry, was one of the best of home remedies and was good for the nerves, good for fever, scrofula, consumption, bad heart and whatnot, good for colds, coughs, and any and every respiratory trouble.

Many a time my mother sent my brother Hugh and me, as boys, into the woods to get some wild cherry bark which she would boil, mix with syrup and give to us for a tonic. We children were "barking" too much around the house at night. I, too, have given it to some of my children with no bad results.

CHERRY BOUNCE

An old-timey drink made by adding cherries, sugar and flavoring spices to hard liquor and left to stand overnight or longer. Dr. Joe McKay of Buie's Creek gave me the recipe years ago. He was our family doctor and delivered us six Green children, always two years apart.

WILD CHERRY FLOWERS

CHICORY *Cichorium intybus*

This is an attractive perennial weed growing anywhere from one to five feet tall with sky blue and sometimes white heads, and scattered along on each side of the highway or in fence jambs or edges of fields. The root was once used as bitter tonic and also as an adulterant for coffee. It was also used in jaundice and liver complaints.

CHINABERRY TREE *Melia azedarach*

Chainy-berry or umbrella tree. A favorite shade tree, native of many parts of Asia and now naturalized in the southern United States. It has lovely sweet flowers in May and its umbrella shape provides good shade. The old folks say, Mr. Mac once told me, that chinaberry trees planted among orchards keep worms and rot away from the fruit trees. Also oil from chinaberry seeds will kill fleas on dogs and vermin generally. A soap made from these berries used to be called "poor man's soap." But the best use of the berries was to make wash for sore eyes, or ointment for scald-head.

CURE FOR DROPSY

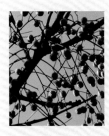

In an old notebook I found the following prescription—"One tablespoon of steel dust, two tablespoons of powdered Virginia snakeroot, two tablespoons of wild ginger root, two of dogwood root bark, two of black Chinaberry tree bark, two of low myrtle root bark, and mix with honey or molasses until liquid-soft. A dose was one half of a teaspoonful three times a day." Then the dose was gradually increased to one teaspoonful three times per day. The patient was ordered to avoid damp air and wet feet. Many a person said he owed his life to this old remedy.

ABOVE: CHINABERRY FRUIT IN NOVEMBER

CHICORY FLOWERS

JACK IN THE BUSH

A GUESSING GAME for two players. The first will extend his closed hand, holding tiny objects. (My brother Hugh and I used grains of corn; some of our neighbors used chinquapins.) The second player is to guess at the number as per the following dialogue:

"Jack in the bush."
"Cut him down."
"How many licks?"

The second player then guesses at the number. The hand is opened revealing the objects—sometimes none at all. If he guesses correctly, he wins all that the hand holds. If he misses, he must pay the first player from his holdings the difference between his guess and the actual number. The game continues till one has cleaned the other out. Of course the supply of grains of corn or chinquapins or whatever is not inexhaustible. At the start, the players agree on the number they have to play with, say twenty-five or fifty.

CHINQUAPIN *Castanea pumila*

Tea from the bark of this bush or tree was used for intermittent fever and chills. The wood is also mighty tough. It makes good fence posts and lasts for generations in the ground. There's many a fence post of it still standing in Little Bethel, though because of the blight the tree is getting scarcer and scarcer. Young girls used to make nice necklaces out of the chinquapin nuts.

COCKLEBUR *Xanthium strumarium var. glabratum*

Cucklebur, sheep-burr. Alternate doses of quinine and tea made of cockleburs (gathered before frost) was used for diphtheria or typhoid fever.
■ *A cocklebur under his saddle—said of one who is excessively irritated.*
■ *Close as a cocklebur in a sheep's wool—hard to move, stingy.*

CRABGRASS *Digitaria sanguinalis*

A luxuriant grass that grows in the farmers' fields and will "take the place" if not ploughed out in time. In the old days the farmers used to

CREASY SALLET FLOWERS, MERRITT'S PASTURE, CHAPEL HILL

keep flocks of geese to eat this grass from their cotton fields.

CREASY SALLET *Barbarea verna*
Upland cress for salad and cooking greens.
🐾 *Early in the spring, often in February, in the fields in the South, Negro women especially can be seen bending down here and there gathering creasy.*

OX-EYE DAISY FLOWER HEAD

CREEPING CHARLIE IN FLOWER

CREEPING CHARLIE *Glecoma hederacea*
A most pestiferous ground ivy also known as gill-o'er-the-ground. It will creep strangling-wise all over your lawn if it's not destroyed. The herbalists say it has fine medicinal value as a stimulant and tonic.
🐾 *Whatever its virtues its knavery outweighs them for me.*

LOVE FORTUNES

The Valley girls, as elsewhere, used to tell love fortunes by reciting a divination rhyme as they plucked the petals away one by one.

"One I love, two I love,
Three I love, I say.
Four I love with all my heart,
Five I cast away.
Six he loves, seven she loves,
Eight they both love.
Nine they come and ten they tarry,
Eleven they court and twelve they marry."

DAISY *Chrysanthemum leucanthemum*
One of our most popular wildflowers, its blossoms adding a cheerful, almost gay, feeling to the landscape in early summer. It grows plentifully in meadows, pastures, and along the roadsides and is widely used in flower beds and lawn borders. There is a belief that a bed of ox-eye daisies planted near the front door will drive away fleas, ticks and other pestiferous insects.
■ *Picking daisies—acting crazy.*
■ *Fresh as a daisy.*
■ *Ups-a-daisy (oops-a-daisy)—often said in jollity when tossing a baby or small child up into the air.*

DANDELION *Taraxacum officinale*

The familiar early spring weed. It grows in woodlands, meadows, fields, along roadsides, anywhere and everywhere. The juice or tea was supposed to be good for children's kidneys. The ground-up dried roots were used as a substitute for coffee.

🐦 *We sometimes gathered it for salads and early greens.*

DOG FENNEL IN FLOWER

DOG FENNEL *Eupatorium capillifolium*

A plant common everywhere, except in the extreme North. Found in waste places and along roadsides. In the old days tea made from its foliage or root was used for all sorts of troubles —nerves, overweight and stomach disorders.

DOGWOOD *Cornus florida*

Flowering dogwood. A small beautiful flowering tree which grows well under larger trees and is common from Canada to Florida and west to Kansas and Oklahoma. Among the Valley people it is perhaps the favorite of all trees and its shower of white blossoms over the landscape in spring is a wonder to behold. In autumn its foliage is a beautiful burnished red. Its berries are succulent food for the birds after the first frost. The wood is close-grained and, when dried out or cured, is almost as hard as iron. The butt of a good-sized tree made a tough and long-lasting maul. Tea made from dried leaves of the tree was once used as a tonic, also as a purgative.

DANDELION FLOWER HEAD

❧ *I've had different explanations for the name "dogwood." One was that because of its hardness daggers were made from it, and dagger-wood became dogwood. Another was that dogs (blocks) used in weaving were made of this wood.*

■ *When the dogwood blooms it is planting time.*

■ *When dogwood leaves are the size of squirrels' ears it is time to plant corn.*

■ *Land where dogwood trees grow well will, when cleared, grow the best cotton.*

■ *Dogwood winter—a cold spell that often comes when the dogwoods are in bloom.*

DOGWOOD TOYS

We children never saw store-bought stilts. We made our own. We'd cut dogwood saplings about five or six feet long, trim them, leaving a six- or eight-inch piece of limb protruding from the sapling some foot or more from the ground. These would serve for us to stand on. With the ends of the saplings tucked under our arms and our feet planted on these binding, cut-off limb extensions, we'd stalk about. And what rough wear and tear on our poor shoes! We couldn't use our tom walkers barefooted. They hurt too much.

Some etymologists say that "juvember" is an Algonquin word for a slingshot. For us boys it meant a beanshooter. And what fun we used to have with our shooters! We could buy our rubber bands from most any store. Then we'd cut a forked dogwood sprout and trim this to the proper length. Next we'd fit a strip of the band to each of the little forks with strings and a small slingshot holder where we'd fit a pebble or a single buckshot, and then aim and pull away. All around now we'd go after the birds and often in our games of war go after one another.

TOP: DOGWOOD FLOWER   *BOTTOM:* DOGWOOD FALL BERRIES

FLEABANE

ELDERBERRY *Sambucus canadensis*

A shrub pretty common in the Valley, the history of which goes way, way back. Ancient Hippocrates (400 B.C.) praised its medicinal virtues, using its tea against colds and throat troubles. The herb doctors declared the berries made a good medicine against nearly every physical ailment or discomfort, including the women's monthlies.

FLEABANE *Erigeron annuus*

Colt's tail. A tea from this plant was used as a stimulant tonic and general health builder. Also it was supposed to be a good cure for gonorrhea.

FRINGE TREE FLOWERS

FRINGE TREE *Chionanthus virginicus*

The flowering ash, also called old man's beard. A sweet-scented shrub common to North Carolina woods. The white beard or fringe of this beautiful tree—perhaps rather a shrub since it rarely grows higher than twenty feet—appears in early spring even before the leaves of the other trees have thickened. Its white beard can be seen here and there in the woods, and its heavenly smell fills the air. It is a showy tree and is often planted by Valley people for ornamentation. Its time of flowering is early April to early May. It grows best in damp land and along stream banks, the botanists say. Tea made from the bark was good for the yawns and gapes. Also it was used for bronchial infections and as a wound cleanser.

🐚 *The many I have planted around our house thrive mightily, though we live on a hill. In the old days the settlers chewed the roots and swallowed the juice, saying it added to their sexual powers. The high birthrate in the Valley—up to recent years—might give credence to this superstition. But I doubt there has ever been any need here for such help.*

GOLDENROD *Solidago spp.*

There are numerous species and all beautiful. When late summer comes, their golden glory adorns the landscape—the roadsides, meadows, pasturelands, and fallow fields.

🐚 *I remember how my English teacher at Buie's Creek Academy loved it, call it flower or call it weed. He wrote a poem about it, and I thought it was wonderful with its rhyming line saying, "It lifts its pale fingers up to God." Later when I grew more critical, I realized that "fingers" was not quite appropriate.*

GOLDENROD: *SOLIDAGO ALTISSIMA*

HEAL ALL *Prunella vulgaris*

Self-heal. An aromatic plant common to fields, woods and waste places especially, in almost all of North America. It is an astringent and also a vulnerary. A decoction from it was supposed to be good for anything, hence its name.

HENBIT *Lamium amplexicaule*

A nettle, often called bee nettle, found in rich wastelands from February to October. Used as a laxative.

HEAL ALL FLOWER HEAD

HENBIT FLOWERS

HEPATICA *Hepatica americana*

An early flowering woodland plant, abundant in the Valley, as in most of North America. Also known as liverwort. Its lobed leaves are liver-shaped, and "hepatic" means liver. Used for liver complaints and also for fevers and coughs.

HEPATICA FLOWER

HICKORY *Carya spp.*

Hickory wood makes the best fire for curing barbecue, smoking meat and also for courting. Burn a hickory log and make a poultice of the ashes for shingles.

❧ *In late fall we children used to have great fun going into the woods with buckets or tow sacks and gathering the nuts that had fallen to the ground, most of them already hulled or partly hulled from striking the earth. And then came the cracking by the fireside and digging the goodies out.*

When I was a little boy, I was told by an old colored man, Uncle Reuben, that if I put a piece of hickory wood in a creek where the water ran swiftly and let it stay there a week or so it would turn into a whetrock. I tried it, and for a week beat a path to the creek. No whetrock. Finally I got disgusted and quit.

- *As tight as hickory bark.*
- *As tough as a hickory stick.*

ROGER AND CORLISS

Then there was the business of Roger Bethune and Corliss Neal. They got into a fight one day in Fayetteville and Corliss broke out one of Roger's eyeteeth, root and all. Being a blacksmith and a toothpuller too, Corliss made Roger a new tooth out of a piece of hickory wood, then drove it in and said, "Now, Roger, you're fixed good as new."

They both were drunk at the time, and of course Corliss was as addled as Roger was. Next day when Roger sobered up, his new eyetooth gave him a fit. The dampness in his mouth had caused it to swell, and soon the side of his face was puffed out as if he'd been stung by a swarm of hornets. He was a looking sight, as they say in the Valley. His wife hurried him fast to town and Doctor Bain, the dentist, nearly tore off his jaw getting that new eyetooth separated from him. Corliss had certainly done a good job.

When the doctor let Roger loose he went straight to the hardware store, bought himself a pistol and went looking for Corliss. But some of their friends stopped him and persuaded him to give up the gun. From that day till he died he and Corliss had no dealings with each other, though before that they had been buddies and loved to get drunk together.

HICKORY NUTS

Left: Holly Tree at Windy Oaks farm   *Right:* Holly berries and leaves

Holly *Ilex opaca*

A popular evergreen tree. It never grows as large or tall as the big oaks and pines, but I have seen a few with bodies eighteen inches in diameter near the ground. In winter when the holly berries are red it is much used for Christmas decoration. A decoction made from the berries was for a long, long time used in the Valley and elsewhere as a good medicine for coughs and colds. Also, the bark of this tree, when chewed, was good for the teeth. The holly bark was much used long ago as a source of bird lime, which was spread on limbs of trees to catch small birds in its viscous, sticky substance.

Sweethearts' Fortunes

The leaves of the holly have little spiny points, and we young folks used to tell fortunes by these spines, especially as to sweethearts. We would start with spine one as *A* and go on down the alphabet to the end.

The catch for me at first was that my girl's name was so far down the alphabet that the spines too often gave out before I got to the letter beginning either her given (Christian) name or surname. But since from my earliest day I have had a devious nature, I got around it by choosing the letter from her name I wanted and so was comforted and with no conscience pang at all.

HONEYSUCKLE *Lonicera japonica*

A pestiferous vine with small white or yellow tubular-shaped blossoms. It seems to thrive under any and all conditions, and nothing it loves better than to wrap its twisting self around newly-planted loblolly pines. Its fruit is a little black berry about the size of a pea and in old days was supposed to be a good emetic as well as cathartic. Very clever of it to have it both ways—or ends.

🐚 *The honeysuckle's heavenly smell even surpasses that of the magnolia—to me it does.*

HORSE NETTLE *Solanum carolinense*

Also called apple of Sodom, bull nettle and wild tomato.

HORSE NETTLE BERRIES

🐚 *This Sodomy pest used to play havoc with our bare feet as children, especially if the dead dried plants chopped up by the hoe were stepped on. The thorns were sharp as little needles.*

LEFT: HONEYSUCKLE FLOWERS *RIGHT*: HONEYSUCKLE VINES

JIMSON WEED FLOWER

JERUSALEM OAK *Chenopodium ambrosioides*
Ambrosia, Mexican tea, wild wormseed or
worm weed, also stinking weed. It is common
throughout the South, July to October, and
grows prolifically in waste places and along
roadsides, sometimes reaching a height of six
feet or more. It is aromatic, and the crushed
stem gives forth a sticky substance. In the old
days women used tea from its seeds to help in
menstruation. Some of the old folklorists
warned against it because, as they said, it had
a "bad poison effect on the brain." The tea was
used to clean out the children's bowels.

*In the Valley we used to burn the plant for
potash to rub on our fresh hog meat. I don't like
this plant, for as a boy I had to grub up too much
of it as it tried to spread into the fields.*

JIMSON WEED *Datura stramonium*
Asthma weed, Jamestown weed, thorn apple.
A heavy-leaved erect poisonous weed with pale-
violet malodorous trumpet-shaped flowers
sometimes referred to as "Angel's Trumpets." It
has spiny seed pods, and these seeds when eaten
can cause death, it is said. It springs up quickly
in neglected vegetable gardens and in waste

"SHO' FINE!"

Dr. Leonard Fields, our family physician for forty years or more, told me of Jimson weed's powers in the treatment of asthma. He had a Negro boy for a patient and was treating him regularly with atropine. Days passed and his patient didn't show up for his regular dose. One day Dr. Fields met him on the street in Chapel Hill and asked him how he was getting along. "Sho' fine," said the boy. Then he pulled out a large half-smoked cigarette. He told the doctor that his grandmother had put him to smoking dried Jimson weed leaves and she was curing him up.

The old woman was right in her treatment, said the doctor. "The weed has the same drug in it with which I had been treating this patient."

places. A tea made from its leaves was supposed to be good to help a mother to a quick recovery from the pains of childbirth. Also it was recommended in the treatment of syphilis. Sometimes the warmed leaves bound against the head were good for headache. Collard or Jimson leaves, wilted in the oven, could take the fever out of risings. A pound of beaten fresh green leaves mixed with three pounds of lard made a good grease-rubbing for women's inflamed breasts.

🐚 *We children used to have great fun in the dusk of warm summer evenings chasing after the great tobacco moths that haunted the strong-scented blooms of the Jimson weed. I read in an old book once where it said that harem wives in Turkey were wont to chew this weed and swallow the juice to strengthen their powers of love. I wonder what the head of the harem, the old Turk himself, chewed.*

JOB'S TEARS *Onosmodium virginianum*
The false gromwell of the forget-me-not family. It grows to a height of three or four feet and is common in the seaboard states from New England to Florida. Its pearly-white capsule-like seeds hanging down suggest tears maybe. The seeds and the root were used as a diuretic in the old days.

🐚 *How Job got connected with it I don't know. Its greatest value to me is its poetic name.*

LADY SLIPPER *Cypripedium acaule*
Lady's slipper or whippoorwill shoes. Known also as moccasin flower, perhaps because of its one flat-headed blossom. It grows from Manitoba to Georgia in swamplands and damp-ish woods. A tincture from its root was once supposed to be good for nervous diseases.

LADY SLIPPER

27

LOBLOLLY PINE

LOBLOLLY PINE *Pinus taeda*

Pine, common old field pine, especially grown now for pulpwood.

LONGLEAF PINE *Pinus palustris*

Long straw or long-needled pine. Once the tree-glory of the Valley as well as most of eastern North Carolina below the fall line. For a long time these trees were sources of income for the people in lumber, turpentine and tar. The great trees are all gone now, save a few patches preserved here and there as on the James Boyd estate in Southern Pines [now the Weymouth Center for the Arts and Humanities]. The stumps of these trees are still a great source of fat lightwood.

🔊 *We children often pinched off brown or yellow bits of hardened turpentine exuding from scarred spots on longleaf pine trees and used them for our chewing gum. We did the same with sweet gum oozings.*

LONGLEAF PINE *TOP:* BOUGHS *BOTTOM:* BUDS[4]

LIGHTWOOD

Fat splinters from the longleaf pine, full of rosin (or turpentine), were good for starting fires under green oak wood and for traveling the dark roads in the black night.

Lightwood knots from the dead limbs of longleaf pine tops were especially full of rosin and, when chopped into bits and pieces, also made wonderful material for starting fires and keeping then going in the fireplace. We used them often in place of lanterns in serenading, bird-blindings, and 'possum and coon hunts.

A TREE THAT SHOOK THE WORLD

When I was a boy, we in the winter were typically busy cutting longleaf pine logs for a bit of income. And what huge trees some of them were! Many of the logs were so large (three and four feet in diameter) that deep gaps had to be cut in them before the logcart-axle could straddle them for hauling.

Down in the swamp of Middle Prong Creek stood one of our pines, unbelievably majestic—twenty-nine feet (I measured it) in circumference and at least a hundred and twenty-five feet high. There was a hornets' nest hanging from its lowest limbs and my brother Hugh and I often with our beanshooters tried to hit it with pebbles, but it was so high up we never could even rouse the hornets out.

In those days trees were meant to be cut down. And so since this giant one was too big for hauling, my father sold it to Mr. Joe Turner

Matthews for five dollars to make shingles out of. It took him and his three sons more than two days to cut it down. Then it was found to be too tough for splitting and so was left to rot.

I was away at school when it was cut, but later Mr. Matthews, with a light in his eyes, told me of the tremendous noise it made on hitting the earth. "Why, Paul," he said, "it shook the world—and the crows and varmints left the swamp same as if an earthquake had struck. A lot of people came to see it fall and they said there'd never been nothing like it." The truth is, I think, Mr. Matthews was more interested in the drama of the great tree's falling than in getting shingles. He was an experienced woodsman and must have known such a monster would not be good shingle-timber.

LONGLEAF PINE TREE

LOVE VINE *Cuscuta campestris*

Dodder or field dodder. It is a leafless parasite with whitish stems.[5] If allowed to have its way, it can overrun a flower bed or border and choke the flowers into a stunted and even wilted condition. It also can play havoc with a wheat or oat crop. Its clinging nature gives it its name. In the old days some of the Valley people found it useful in treating sick cows and mules.

LOVE VINE

LEFT: FIELD OF LYRE-LEAVED SAGE   *RIGHT:* LYRE-LEAVED SAGE FLOWERS

MAGNOLIA FLOWER

LYRE-LEAVED SAGE *Salvia lyrata*

This plant grows in most parts of the United States and is common in North Carolina. Its big lyre-shaped leaves give it its name. It flourishes in sandy woods and barrens and is conspicuous for its lavender blooms. Sometimes called cancer weed, its juice is used to remove warts and cancerous growths.

Was used, I should say, for now in our more enlightened days we have the surgeon's knife and chemotherapy.

MAGNOLIA *Magnolia grandiflora*

A beautiful and popular shade tree throughout the Valley and the south. It has become a sort of cognomen for the culture, the beauty and the old-timeyness of the region.

MAGNOLIA LEAF: A FETISH TOKEN

Galley Farrington, who works for me now and then, told me recently of his experience with a magnolia leaf and the woman who used it.

"SHE CAME DRIVING down there to the store," he said, "where a lot of us fellows were chewing the rag, this woman did, and whew! what a knock-out she was. She smelled high of cologne and had some sort of brass earrings big as silver dollars in her ears. She said that she was out to bring joy to mankind."

MAGNOLIA LEAVES AND SEED POD

" 'You all fellows are always broke, ain't you?' she said. We agreed that was mostly true. 'Well,' she said, 'I can show you how never to be broke. See these magnolia leaves,' and then out of her big wove handbag she pulled a lot of magnolia leaves.

" 'If you will take one of these here leaves,' she said, 'and put a dollar bill on it and fold it up inside, put it in your pocket, you'll always have good luck and you'll never be broke for you'll have that dollar. But mostly and the main thing,' she said, 'is you'll have good luck. Who's got a dollar?'

"Some of us had a dollar. I just happened to have one bill so I handed it to her.

"She folded it up in the leaf into a tight little wad and handed it back to me.

" 'Now put that in your pocket, honey,' she said, 'and keep it there and the first thing you know good luck will start happening.'

"Two or three of the other fellows had dollar bills and fool-like—just like me—they handed them over to that woman and saw her fold 'em into the leaf and hand it back to them.

" 'Now you see,' she said, 'I ain't charging a penny for my service. I just want to do good to my fel-lowman. Now you all boys,' she said, 'don't touch them leaves in your pocket for the next hour. Let 'em stay in there and get 'climated to your body. Then it's all right to feel them. And good luck to you all boys now and I'm on my way to help other folks.' And she got into her late Ford roadster and drove off.

"It was Satiddy time and we didn't have to go to work anywhere and so we stood around chewing the rag some more and still smelling the heavy scent of that woman that was gone off. Maybe it was that scent that made us play the fool. Anyhow, after about a' hour by the clock on the Home Savings building we pulled out our magnolia leaves, opened them and, dang my soul, there was no dollar bill in any of them.

"That woman had really reamed us. We saw her driving sassy around Chapel Hill several times after that and far as I know she might have reamed some of them smart professors. Anyhow we were so ashamed to be made fools of by her that we didn't call the cops in to arrest her."

MAIDEN'S BLUSHES

MARSH PINK FLOWER

MAIDEN'S BLUSHES *Pinckneya pubens*

Something of a subtropical shrub which grows from North Carolina to Florida. It prefers wet, boggy soil. Its greenish and pale yellow capsules grow in thick clusters among the leaves. In the autumn these mellowing leaves become ruddy-tinged, therefore the gothic name, which to me is the most important thing about the plant. In the old days it was used like Peruvian bark (quinine) for intermittent fevers.

MARSH PINK *Sabatia spp.*

A lovely little flower common to bogs and moist soil. This herb is a good tonic and is said to have been used in the old days as a substitute for quinine.

MAY APPLE FLOWER

MAY APPLE *Podophyllum peltatum*

Also mandrake or wild lemon. A big-leaved, low-growing plant common in the Valley. It has an evil-smelling white bloom which produces one "apple" about the size of a large bullace or musket ball. It was used as a cathartic and also for numerous diseases like most every plant in the Valley.

MEADOW BEAUTY *Rhexia mariana*

A charming little flower, as beautiful as its name, much like a scarlet evening primrose if there were such a thing. The leaves have a sweetish acid taste and are tasty to deer. Therefore, sometimes this meadow beauty is called deer grass although it is not a grass at all.

MEADOW BEAUTY FLOWERS

MEADOW PARSNIP *Zizia aurea*

This plant grows in the upland woods as well as along the river flood plains. It is mainly found in the Piedmont and the mountains but there is enough of it in the Valley to make itself noticed. A tincture of this plant used to be used as a nerve irritant and also in the treatment of syphilis. Tea drunk from it makes a person sweat profusely.

MEADOW RUE *Thalictrum revolutum*

This plant is of the crowfoot family and has a graceful drooping foliage and small white flowers which appear in April or May. The roots of the plant have been used as a purgative and also for sciatica and snakebites. It is supposed to be poisonous to stock for it contains an alkaloid.

MILKWEED *Asclepias syriaca*

There are numerous kinds of milkweed in the Valley and all are noted for their juicy milky stalks and for their feathery seeds that blow easily in the wind.

We children used to have more fun taking the seed pods and running in front of each other and blowing the downy stuff into one another's faces.

LEFT: MEADOW PARSNIP FLOWERS   *RIGHT:* MILKWEED PODS WITH SEEDS

THE MISTLETOE BOUGH

Along with the piteous "In the Baggage Coach Ahead" and "The Fatal Wedding," my mother introduced us children to this song-story. I recently came across its words and music in Vance Randolph's Organ Folksongs.

The mistletoe hung in the castle hall,
The holly branch shone on the old oak wall.
The baron's retainers were blithe and gay,
Keeping the Christmas holiday.
The baron beheld with a father's pride
While she with her bright eyes seemed to be
The star of that goodly company.
Oh, the mistletoe bough!

"I'm weary of dancing now," she cried,
"Here tarry a moment, I'll hide, I'll hide,
And, Lovell, be sure thou are the first to trace
The clue to my secret lurking place."
Away she ran and her friends began
Each tower to search and each nook to scan,
And young Lovell cried, "Oh where dost thou hide?

I'm lonesome without thee, my own dear bride."
Oh, the mistletoe bough!

They sought her that night, they sought her next day,
They sought her in vain when a week passed away.
In the highest, the lowest, the loneliest spot
Young Lovell sought wildly, but found her not.
And years flew by, and their grief at last
Was told as a sorrowful tale long past,
And when Lovell appeared the children cried,
"See the old man weeps for his fairy bride."
Oh, the mistletoe bough!

At length an oak chest that had long laid hid
Was found in the castle, they raised the lid
When a skeleton form lay moldering there
In the bridal wreath of that lady fair.
Oh sad was her fate, when in sportive jest
She hid from her lord in the old oak chest.
It closed with a spring and a dreadful doom,
And the bride lay clasped in a living tomb.
Oh, the mistletoe bough!

MISTLETOE *Phoradendron serotinum*
A romantic parasitic plant that grows mainly on oak trees. The leaves of the mistletoe have been chewed to relieve toothache, and it is said that more than one person has died from eating the berries. I have never known of a case myself. Some of the old people used to put the leaves between the children's toes to cure ground itch.

🪶 *It is especially popular at Christmas time and young people, even old ones, hang up sprays of mistletoe about the house. When a person happens to be under one of these sprays, another person has the privilege of kissing him or her.*

MISTLETOE

35

Mountain Laurel

Monkshood *Aconitum uncinatum*
Trailing monkshood, wolfbane. A poisonous aconite, it grows in moist and shady places and has been used in the treatment of gout and rheumatism.

Mountain Laurel *Kalmia latifolia*
Although mainly limited to the mountains of North Carolina, the mountain laurel has escaped—maybe the seeds were carried by birds or freshets—and is found growing here and there far down in the Valley, especially on the north side of hilly stream banks.[6] The leaves are supposed to be narcotic and poisonous to both man and beast, but preparations from them used to be good treatment for diarrhea and skin eruptions.

MULBERRY *Morus spp.*

A common fruit in the Valley for feeding hogs and children.

🐚 *On our farm we used to have two kinds of mulberries, the white and the black, and in the early spring we children watched the trees with avid appetites. As soon as the berries were beginning to get ripe, we would climb up and stuff ourselves and then we had plenty of trouble with diarrhea. We boys used to use the inner bark of the tree to make whips, calf traces, swings, jumping ropes, and so on.*

■ *When the mulberry buds appear, the frost is over.*

■ *"His face turned as purple as a goose's ass in mulberry time."*

MULLEIN LEAVES

MULLEIN *Verbascum thapsus*

Achilles' Heel or Adam's Flannel. A common plant throughout the valley. It loves to grow in fence jambs and along the roadsides and grows up to the height of a man's head or beyond and has a whitish fuzzy bloom. It was sometimes called Indian tobacco since the Indians were wont to smoke the leaves. The tea of this mullein was especially good for stomach pains in children. The warmed leaves, as in the case of Jimson weed or collard leaves, placed on sores and poisoned places were considered, and still are, a good remedy to bring down swelling. Another good folk medicine from mullein used to be to take the root of the mullein, stew it along with wild cherry bark, brown sugar and a little vinegar, and then keep it on hand for colds and coughs. The oil from its blooms used to be recommended for earache. According to one book I read, the Romans called the mullein "candelaria" from their custom of taking the long dry stalks and dipping them in suet or some kind of oil and using them as funeral torches. The Greeks were supposed to utilize the leaves for lamp wicks.

🐚 *Many a young girl in the Valley has been wont to make her cheeks pretty and pink by rubbing her face with the velvety leaves.*

MULBERRY IN FRUIT

MUSCADINE GRAPES

MUSCADINE *Vitis rotundifolia*

Bullace. Wild black grapes about the size of a marble that used to grow plentifully in the Valley. Much the same as the white scuppernong.[7] After frost they were black as the ace of spades and sweet as sugar. It's hard to find any wild bullaces anywhere in the Valley these days. Their history goes far back. When Amadas and Barlow first reached the shores of North Carolina in 1584, they spoke of the wonderful smell of grapes.

In late September we used to climb the viney trees here and there and eat and eat until our heads swam. We children for lack of jumping ropes used to cut bullace vines and use them with great joy, never once thinking that we were under-privileged because we didn't have a nice woven rope bought from a store. "Bullaces grow sweetest when the vines hang on or climb up pine trees," says my friend Nathan Williams.

■ *It is said that grape seeds will cause appendicitis.*

NEW JERSEY TEA *Ceanothus americanus*

More of a shrub than a flower. It grows plenti-fully in dry woods or gravelly places. In mid-summer its white feathery flower centers show up clearly. The Indian doctors used this plant for the treatment of wounds and venereal sores.

NEW JERSEY TEA

NUT GRASS *Cyperus spp.*

A most cantankerous field pest. It is reputed to be so tough that farmers burning it say it reseeds itself from the smoke. Many a farmer has cursed the day this pest got started on his farm.

❧ *I know from much experience of hoeing, chopping, digging and burning the stuff. We'd do that and then the next morning there its little evil green heads would be peeping up out of the earth again.*

NUT GRASS

TOUGH STUFF

"Yessir," said Emmet Ennis to me one day, "there's many a tough thing in this Cape Fear River Valley, Mr. Paul, many a tough thing. You've heard of whit leather. You've heard of dried sweet gum trees, of seasoned dogwood, or black gum trees that neither lightning nor dynamite can split–but I'll tell you there's nothing as hard to wear down and out and get rid of as this here nut grass that grows in the fields. Ma and Pa fought it for many years.

"Now old Judge Hinton had told Pa that hogs would kill it. So Pa tried hogs for years. The hogs would root and dig and get after this stuff and then when we thought we'd got it whipped and started corn or cotton there, out it would come thick as ever. Finally Pa said to me when I was a little teeny boy, 'Son, there's nothing to do but move off and leave this stuff. Let it take over.' So we decided to let that land lie out and the pines grow up and take it.

"Well sir, twenty years went by and the woods growed up over the place and of course the nut grass disappeared. We sold that timber off for pulpwood and got a bulldozer to push up the stumps and went back to farming the land – twenty years now, later! Do you hear me! Well sir, what do you think? That nut grass come up thick as hairs on a dog's back that spring. The stuff had been lying deep in the ground just waiting its time.

"So we give up the fields again and when you drive by my place you'll see thick young pine timber growing there again. Won't be long before we'll sell that timber off but, believe you me, we won't try to farm that place – we'll plant new pine seedlings on it. Yessir, take it from me, nut grass is the toughest stuff the world has ever seen!"

TAIL IN A SPLIT

To be in an embarrassing or difficult situation. Another form of this is "to have one's tail in a split stick." I remember long time ago when we would go possum hunting and were lucky enough to catch a possum. We would cut down a little oak sapling, drive the axe through it to split it and put the possum's tail in that split, release the sides and let them close in on the tail. Then, with the little pole over our shoulders, and the possum behind out of reach of biting us, we would march proudly home.

PARTRIDGEBERRY

OAK *Quercus spp.*

A popular and prolific shade tree in the Valley. There are several kinds of oak, the most beautiful perhaps being the white oak , though some people prefer the willow or water oak. There is also the red oak, the black jack oak and the chestnut oak.

The inside of oak bark was used to make poultices and teas and tinctures and decoctions for all sorts of diseases. Tea from oak bark was also a drink good for a child's diarrhea, and a good preventive for bed sores was to bathe the tender place with water in which the oak bark had been boiled. It was supposed to be good for rheumatism, boils, neuralgia and all sorts of diseases, too.

Before the no-fence law came into effect in the Valley the farmers let both their cattle and hogs run loose in the woods, the cattle to feed on reeds and other pickings and the hogs to fatten on acorns in the fall. A brag-porker was one fattened on acorns.

■ *Great oaks from little acorns grow.*
■ *Little strokes fell great oaks.*
■ *As sturdy as an oak.*
■ *As stately as an oak.*

PARTRIDGEBERRY *Mitchella repens*

Turkleberry or turkeyberry, sometimes called love-in-winter, pipsissewa, wintergreen, etc. A shy little ground creeper which grows in the moist deep woods. It has delicate fragrant flowers which develop into single red berries that look like little drops of coral among the greenery. The deer especially like these berries and sometimes it is called deer-berry. The berries are good for all kinds of diseases, especially for diarrhea and rheumatism, so say the herb doctors.

PASSIONFLOWER

PASSIONFLOWER *Passiflora incarnata*

Maypop. The purple bloom of this flower is one of the most beautiful imaginable, and it has taken on a certain sort of symbolism in which the center of the big purple bloom represents the Trinity surrounded by the Twelve Apostles. Go out into the fields in May or June and see for yourself in studying the bloom.

In the late summer it bears a soft pulpy fruit about the size of an egg.

The juice squeezed from the leaves and dried made a good medicine for croup and children's pains. A poultice made of warm leaves was also good for neuralgia and the toothache.

🐾 *When it is well-ripened and yellow, the pulpy watery insides are sweet to the taste and good for eating, much like the ripened pawpaw, as we children proved with many a tight bellyful.*

MAYPOP WARS

We boys used to have great fun especially on Sundays when we'd slip away from the old folks and go far down in the corn fields where the maypops, after the crops were laid by, were growing all over the ground with their oblong pods of fruit. We would gather these maypops and organize ourselves in opposing parties and go to it, throwing these at one another. As a boy I visited some friends up near Kipling, and these boys made fun of us who played war with maypops. They played war with rocks. I got in the war with them and the first thing I knew a big rock had laid me out pretty cold when it hit me on the side of the head. From then on my admiration for the Kipling boys was unbounded. *ABOVE:* MAYPOP

TOP: PAWPAW FLOWERS *BOTTOM:* PAWPAW PATCH

PAWPAW *Asimina triloba*

Custard apple. A charming little shrub which has pretty much disappeared from the Valley. Some people are allergic to the fruit and after eating it have been known to break out in a rash.

❧ *Why the plant is disappearing I don't know. It just happens that I am lucky in having one growing wild at my back door. It was there when I moved out in the country and is still flourishing.*

PEACH *Prunus persica*

The common fruit in the Valley and especially in the Sandhills where the fruit is grown commercially. A tincture of the leaves mixed with tobacco juice used to make a flavoring for children's medicine, and the mixture was even better if mixed with snuff. The leaves were used in the old days for tanning leather as well as for making poultices. Sometimes these leaves were warmed and worn as a bandage for headache and other pains. Peach kernels, pounded and made into a sort of oil, were good for earache. A drop of the oil, made by burning a branch of the peach tree with a pine knot or lightwood splinter, on a sore tooth gave help. A dose of this was also good for worms in children.

❧ *Mother used to put peach leaves in her jelly jars to add to the flavor.*

PENNYROYAL *Hedeoma pulegiodes*

Pennr'ile or penny ock. A common aromatic little plant often used to keep away chiggers and fleas. Also pennyroyal tea was used as a sure cure for making the measles break out.

❧ *According to my old friend Mr. Mac, many of the pregnant women in the Valley used the pennyroyal tea as a good preventative against morning nausea. I remember that my own mother often*

PEPPERMINT

put some of the plants in the room on the floor and in the corners to keep out ticks and fleas. We would smear or crush the tiny leaves in our hands and rub our bare legs and feet.

PEPPERGRASS *Lepidium virginicum*
A native annual in the Valley, it can be seen widely spread in the fields and along the road-sides from May to November.

🐚 *Our bare ankles used to get a tingle as we would tramp through this in the summertime.*

PEPPERMINT *Mentha piperita*
A popular herb for the housewife's garden. A widely spreading plant in the Valley, highly aromatic, sometimes also called spearmint.[8]

🐚 *Many a young man has chewed it as he was on his way to see his sweetheart, thus making his breath sweet, and for a purpose.*

PERSIMMONS

PERSIMMON *Diospyros virginiana*
Usually pronounced 'simmon. Often called
'possum apple. A popular wild fruit in the
Valley. A liquid concoction from the inner bark
of the persimmon tree is supposed to be one
of the best gargles for ulcerated or sore throats.
🐛 *According to Uncle Beverly Lassiter, he has
stopped many a coming bad cold by use of this
gargle.*
■ *As sour as a green 'simmon.*
■ *Possum over my persimmon. That's a huckle-
berry over my persimmon. (One thing topping
another, or one thing too deep for solving.)*
■ *A large crop of acorns and berries and persimmons
is a sign of a hard winter.*

PERSIMMON BEER

One of our best drinks used to be 'simmon
beer, a good tonic for both children and
grown-ups. I remember when I was a boy we
used to make up a big keg or small barrel of it
at our house. We'd mash up, say, a bushel of
ripe persimmons after the first frost had struck
them, mix that well with one-half bushel of
wheat bran, and sometimes we would mash up
sweet potatoes. Then we'd add some twelve
gallons of fresh spring water and three or four
ounces of hops. Next we'd take a clean barrel,
cover the bottom with broomstraw up to
a few inches above the spigot level and lay a
few dozen ripe honey locusts on the straw.
Then we would pour the new mixture into the
barrel and let it stand three or four weeks in
a warm place.

    If we wanted to, we'd draw the beer off, put
it in jugs or bottles and store it in a cool place.
From then on we were supposed to have a fine
beverage for our table and for our friends on
any occasion. Man never could drink enough
to get drunk on it, and now that legitimate
beer has come in, making of persimmon beer
has just about passed out.

PERSIMMON FLOWER

PICKERELWEED *Pontederia cordata*
An attractive perennial that grows in watery places in the swamps, usually reaching from one to four feet in height with showy spikes of blue flowers. A tea made from the root is supposed to be a good cathartic. The plant is becoming very popular for garden pools.

❧ *My wife and I planted several of them near a spring below the house.*

PILEWORT

PILEWORT *Erechtites hieracifolia*
Fireweed. This plant springs up plentifully in new ground after it has been burnt over. Sometimes if left alone it will grow to a height of eight or ten feet and then spread its silky white blossoms[9] to the air. It is easy to kill. The name derives from its use in treating piles (hemorrhoids).

TOP: PICKERELWEED FLOWERS   *BOTTOM:* PICKERELWEED

PINE *Pinus spp.*

A common lumber and pulpwood tree in North
Carolina. There are many species: longleaf pine,
shortleaf, loblolly, rosemary and so on. In the
old days eastern North Carolina was a great
stretch of longleaf pine forests. Not only was
the pine once the source of tar, pitch, turpentine
and lumber—and, in these later days, of pulpwood—but it was also the source of many folk
cures. A cure, for instance, for influenza was to
take several doses of warm water in which the
inner skin of the pine bark had been soaked.
Some old people would say the cure was no
good unless the tree was skinned on the north
side. Turpentine, tar oil, and tar salve were used
for every sort of ailment. It would take pages
to describe the ways and uses of the pine trees.
Books have already been written on the subject.

❧ *When I was a boy, in driving from home
down to Dunn, we would often pass turpentine
stills here and there with the smoke rising from
them like a fog.*

*Thrash doctors would use the pinetops for some
of their hocus-pocus cures, and I've known of
cases where the quack doctors would put pine
bows under the sick person's bed to help towards
convalescence.*

PINE STRAW CHORES

In rainy weather we
used to get the dread-
ful news from our father
who would come out
and announce, "Well,
boys, while it is wet, we
better rake pine straw."

So into the woods
we'd go and rake and rake and haul the dead
pine needles to put into the mule stables and
into the cow stables for bedding. And in the
spring these stables would be cleaned out and
the manure taken into the fields.

Another use for pine straw was for hilling
our potatoes. When the first frost came, we
would go into the potato patch and cut away
the vines and then with a turn-plough, plough
up the potatoes and sort them out and then
hill them. These hills usually contained some
fifteen to twenty-five bushels piled cone-like,
covered with pine straw and then covered with
dirt with an opening at the top like an Indian's
teepee. Sometimes we would put a shelter over
these hills. We were always aghast when we
opened these hills to see how many of our
potatoes had rotted.

ABOVE: LONGLEAF PINE WITH CONES

THE LEGEND OF THE GYPSY PINE

I was just a boy when I first saw gypsies, the dark-
skinned itinerant people who used to appear
from time to time in the Valley in small bands.

They traveled by horse and wagon conveyances,
later by automobiles and usually worn-out ones at
that. They told fortunes and were supposed to be
unconscionable thieves, especially devastating as to
chickens and sometimes even stealing babies.

Just below Buie's Creek once stood a great pine-
tree. Professor H.F. Page first pointed it out to me.
It was called the gypsy pine, and he wrote a poem
about it. It had a great hollow cut out of it where
the gypsies chipped out lightwood for their camp-
fires nearby. It finally collapsed under the chipping
and lay rotting away. Both it and the gypsies are
gone now.

PIPSISSEWA

PIPSISSEWA *Chimaphila maculata*
Sometimes called ground holly, love-in-winter, rheumatism weed, or wintergreen. A delicious and fragrant little flower that grows in the deep woods. With its shiny evergreen foliage and its dainty summer blossoms, it is one of the most beautiful woodflowers in the Valley. Pipsissewa is evidently an Indian name and, according to some, it refers to the strengthening properties which the red men ascribed to it. It goes by many names. A tea made from its leaves is supposed to be a very healthful tonic.

PITCHER PLANT *Sarracenia spp.*
Side-saddle plant. A strange and striking plant that grows in the deep wet swamps of the Valley. The leaves are various colors from green to striped yellow or even deep red, and the blossoms are most unusual, usually of a dead dull red rose color, although I have found some completely yellow ones. The inside of the flower exudes a sweet secretion and many an insect in search of this sweetness finds himself a helpless prisoner unable to escape up the inside of the blossom because of the opposing bristles.[10]
The Indians used this pitcher plant to make a tea for the smallpox, and the Scotch settlers in the Valley fed a tincture of it to their children

as an internal remedy. According to an old prescription, one ounce of pitcher plant root to one quart of water; one tablespoon given to the sick child every four or five hours would result in a cure.

🐚 *We used to go down into the swamp about a half a mile northwest of our house and gather great handfuls of these strange flowers in June.*

TOP: RED PITCHER PLANT LEAVES (*SARRACENIA PURPUREA*)
BOTTOM: YELLOW PITCHER PLANT FLOWER (*SARRACENIA FLAVA*)

POISON IVY *Rhus radicans*

Pizen ivy. A woody nature shrub as well as a climbing vine. It grows anywhere and everywhere it is allowed to grow and is a source of serious skin poison to most people.

So far as I know, time is about the best cure for the infection, though many Valley people say that a tomato cut in two and rubbed on the infected part will bring relief.

When my wife and I built our house near Chapel Hill years ago, we found the woods infested with it. The tall white oaks around the spring we walled up were overrun with the stuff, and it took the work of several men two weeks to cut the vines away and burn them. Some of the "vines" I measured were four to six inches in diameter.

POISON IVY

POISON SUMAC *Rhus vernix*

A prolific shrub that grows in the Valley anywhere from six to eighteen feet tall. It is most commonly found along the edges of damp swamps and it blooms in June. The fruit of the poison sumac is whitish or dun-colored and the harmless sumac fruit is red.[11] It is said to be a stimulant and a narcotic in rheumatism and herpes.

POISON SUMAC, FALL COLOR

POKEWEED *Phytolacca americana*

Poke weed, pokeberry weed, poke. It is found almost everywhere from Canada and the Dakotas down toward Florida. The young shoots are often used for salad or a substitute for asparagus. One of the best folk remedy plants in the Valley. One ounce of dried root mixed with a pint of water and two tablespoons given as a dose was supposed to be a good treatment for chronic syphilis. An ointment made from the root was good for all kinds of skin diseases, and if the ointment was mixed with lard and the children's heads rubbed with it at night, every nit and louse would soon disappear. Indian runners on long journeys used to chew the leaves to quench the thirst, so it was said. Pokeroot tea was especially good for hog

---

POKE SALAT

My friend, Mr. Mac the miller, told me this story. "Take the case of old McIntyre Prewett who lived down near Linden. He lived to be so old that in his later years he walked like he was squatting down, and when he couldn't walk anymore, he lay up in his little house there, nothing but a bedful of bones, and dreened as dry of life as a basket of chips. After he quit moving and breathing any at all the neighbors waited a week to be sure he was dead and then they buried him.

"You ask me how old he was? I don't know. Some say he was a hundred, some say he was a hundred and twenty-five. Anyhow, I remember his telling me once when I was a shirt-tailed boy about the time George Washington drove through the country there to the east and all the people in Tarboro went wild and fired off their one-pound cannon in celebration —yes, he said he was a grown young man hisself at the time.

"And you know what made him live so long? I asked him that once, and he looked at me out of his little squeezed, squinched-up eyes and he said, 'Why, poke salat, poke salat.'

"They say he used to eat it by the peck. Then in the wintertime he lay up like a bear and drank cornmeal gruel made with water.

"Yessir, I recommend poke salat and meal gruel for these vitamin folks. Dang sight more sense in it I fully do believe—and they're cheaper too, much cheaper."

ABOVE: POKEWEED, EARLY SPRING

---

cholera. The leaves and the berries (sometimes called pigeonberries) and the roots are purgative and narcotic. A tincture of the ripe berries has been used as a popular remedy for chronic rheumatism, and the juice has been used for tumors, cancer, hermorrhoids and for all kinds of troubles.

POOR MAN'S WEATHERGLASS

Anagallis arvensis

Pimpernel or common pimpernel. It grows from eastern Canada down eastern United States to Mexico. It is poisonous to dogs and horses but is supposed to be sexually stimulating to humans. Its red flowers appear in midsummer and are open only in bright sunshine. They close up at the approach of a storm, hence, the name for the plant.

POKEWEED BERRIES

POSSUM HAW BERRIES

POSSUM HAW *Viburnum nudum*

Sometimes called 'possum grape. This slender shrub, rarely becoming large enough to be called a tree, grows plentifully in swamps and along streams.

੭ৣ *We boys used to love to eat the blue-ripened berries. We still have a plentiful supply of these haws around our spring below the house.*

PURSLANE *Portulaca oleracea*

A curse in many a garden. This much-branched radiating annual is prolific as crabgrass and as common in all of the dry and sandy soils and waste grounds of the Valley. It flowers in July and according to a book I read, like many other plants, it is good for nearly everything under the sun medicinally, being "emetic, expectorant, cathartic, diaphoretic, astringent, rubefacient, blistering, stimulant and is used in dropsy and as a powerful external stimulant." The Indians used it as a purgative

੭ৣ *My father used to have us children pull it from the garden to feed to the hogs.*

PURSLANE

PYXIE PLANT *Pyxidanthera barbulata var. brevifolia*
Pyxie moss. A shy little flower that is rarely
found anywhere except in scattered places in the
Carolina sandhills.

QUAKER LADIES *Houstonia caerulea*
Bluets or innocence. This modest and demure
little flower is one of the earliest to appear in
the spring. Unlike most flowers in the Valley, it
seems to have no medicinal virtues.
❧ *When warm spring came in March, we children were always on the lookout for these quaker
ladies. Their arrival meant that winter was
passed and we could go barefoot again.*

PYXIE PLANT

QUAKER LADIES

51

QUEEN ANNE'S LACE

LITTLE BIG MEN

We boys used to get the dried autumn leaves of rabbit tobacco and roll them into "cigarettes." We'd puff away and walk about in braggadocio. Little big men. Now and then we'd flick away an invisible ash with a delicate and dandyish finger. The leaves made good chewing tobacco, too, and we'd get a cheek full, roll it about with our tongues, simulating one of our favorite pitchers, and spit profusely about us.

QUEEN ANNE'S LACE *Daucus carota*
Bird's nest, devil's plague, wild carrot.
A tremendously prolific wild plant that colors the hedges and whole fields white with its lacy, delicate blossoms in spring and summer. The root of the plant has been recommended as a poultice for ulcers and even for dropsy.

RABBIT TOBACCO *Gnaphalium obtusifolium*
Cudweed, everlasting, life everlasting, pearly everlasting, featherweed, fussy gussy, sweet balsam. A native annual that grows from one to three feet tall. It has numerous white flowers and is slightly aromatic. It flourishes along roadsides, hedges and in deserted fields. It was used as a tea in the treatment of colds.

RAGWEED *Ambrosia artemisiifolia*
Carrot weed. A prolific weed throughout the Valley and the curse to hay fever victims through the summer. The old people used to think that ragweed would cure warts. Maybe it would.

TOP: RABBIT TOBACCO. *BOTTOM:* RAGWEED

Rattlebox Weed *Crotilaria spp.*

Rattleweed, the common wild pea. It is supposed to be poisonous to horses, but tea made from this and fed to a sick cow was supposed to restore her appetite.

 We children used to pluck the dry pods and shake them close to our ears and listen with delight at the little seeds rattling within.

Rattlesnake Plantain *Goodyera pubescens*

This pretty tufted, white, vein-leaved plant appears in all parts of the Valley. It has been reputed to be a cure for hydrophobia and snakebite. Legend tells that the Indians had such faith in its virtues that they were not afraid of snakebites at all and, when bitten, would apply these leaves to the wound and soon go on as if nothing had happened.

Red Birch[12] *Betula nigra*

The birch common in the Valley as contrasted with the white birch which is better suited to cold climates. The red birch grows along the river banks and creek banks and used to be used widely in making furniture, outdoor seats and tables.

 I remember as a boy how I admired this sort of furniture, and several times my brother and I went down to the old overgrown Sexton millpond place and cut red birch saplings and built some of this furniture for outdoor seats. Later it all rotted away and we lost interest in it.

Redbud Tree *Cercis canadensis*

Judas tree. It seems there are many kinds of trees on which poor Judas hanged himself, but this particular one is the only one I know that has his name. It is a beautiful decorative tree and in

REDBUD TREE IN FLOWER

the early spring it is one of the first to put out its shower of rosy blooms. A tea made from the bark of this tree is supposed to be good for kidney trouble, especially kidney trouble in children. Also it is recommended for grownups' obstructions in the liver and the spleen.

Red Oak *Quercus rubra*

A common tree in the Valley. The bark from this tree is good for all sorts of troubles and diseases. We used to put the bark in the watering troughs for the chickens. If they drank the water, it was supposed to make them lay more eggs.

My father also used to keep red oak bark strips in his hog troughs to help keep off the cholera.

Royal Fern *Osmunda regalis*

A widely diffused fern found on almost any damp place in the Valley. It is easy to transplant and many flower gardens now show it flourishing. Tea made from its root was supposed to be good for coughs and rheumatism.

White Swelling

I remember when I had a case of osteomyelitis or "white swelling," one of the remedies proposed by many neighbors was to boil red oak bark and mix with cornmeal to make a poultice. My mother did that. And I used to carry that heavy poultice wrapped around my right arm. For a while it helped me—as long as I thought it did. Then when I realized it didn't, there was no help at all.

Mrs. Hockaday at Angier said that one of the reasons I decided it didn't help me was because we failed to get the original bark from the north side of the tree and we should have put sugar in it.

Royal Fern   *Left:* early spring fiddleheads *Right:* leaves, early summer

RUE *Ruta graveolens*

Herb of grace. An aromatic plant of popular medicinal use also by the Valley people in the old days. Rue tea was especially good for rheumatism and aching joints.

🐛 *We think of poor mad Ophelia's flower chant in the play Hamlet:*

> *"There's fennel for you, and columbines.*
> *There's rue for you, and here's some for me.*
> *We may call it herb of grace o' Sundays."*

RUE

RUE ANEMONE *Thalictrum thalictroides*

Anemone or windflower. A beautiful shy little flower of the early spring. Like most of its sisters, it too had its medicinal uses in the old days. It was both a purgative and a diuretic.

RUNNING CEDAR *Lycopodium flabelliforme*

Christmas club moss or ground cedar. A crawling cedar found in the deep rich damp woods and used plenteously for decoration at Christmastime.

TOP: RUE ANEMONE. *BOTTOM:* RUNNING CEDAR

ST. JOHN'S-WORT *Hypericum spp.*

A prolific little plant rarely growing beyond two feet in height. Its bright yellow flowers are noticeable in waste fields and along the roadsides nearly all the summer. It was named, I am told, because it was common to gather it on St. John's Eve and to hang it at doors and windows against thunder and evil spirits. There was a belief that on St. John's night the soul had power to leave the body and visit the spot where it would finally be summoned from its earthly habitation. The medicinal properties of St. John's-wort have been extolled. It was said that an ointment made from its blossoms was good for cuts and wounds of any kind, also a tea made from it was designated *fuga daemonum*, a purgative for demons. It was once supposed to be a good remedy for melancholia.

SASSAFRAS *Sassafras albidum*

Ague, ague tree, sassafrack, saxifras. A common small tree found throughout the Valley. The sassafras has an ancient and honorable history. It was especially fancied in late Elizabethan England because of Sir Walter Raleigh's colonists on Roanoke Island sending back sassafras bark and roots to be used medicinally. In the Valley we used to make tea out of the roots and it was supposed to be a very healthful drink. Sometimes it was good to thin the blood of children who were too bouncing and cherry-faced. The doctors would prescribe sassafras tea in the old days rather than prescribing bleeding since it was supposed to thin the blood. The Negroes would often drink sassafras tea in the spring of the year for bad blood.

Blind Staggers

A disease of horses or mules. It is the same as sleepy staggers. There are numerous cures or medicines for this from kerosene oil to turpentine. One that was common in the Valley was very much like the medicine or therapeutic treatment I found described in some papers of my great-great-great-grandfather, Colonel Alexander McAllister, in Cumberland County. His prescription went as follows: "Take one ounce of camphyre dissolved in spirits, this to be squirted up their nostrils at the end of every two hours – a teaspoonful of it also to be put in their ears three times a day: a teaspoonful in each ear and every time the camphyre and spirits is squirted up their nostrils there must be tobacco smoke blew up their nostrils by a smoking pipe. Then take tobacco and tar, set them on fire and smoke the creatures head over it three times a day and give them for their drink tea made of sassafras root and dogwood root. This by diligent attendance is given for certain cure."

Sawtooth Briar *Rubus hispidus*

A mean low-running briar that infests the fields and the hedges. We children used to get our bare feet entangled in it and so we learned to say fierce cusswords very early.

Saxifrage *Saxifraga virginiensis*

A little tough-growing plant, which from its name implies it is supposed to be so powerful that its roots can break rocks apart. Tea from its roots was used for stomach ache.

Scuppernong *Vitis rotundifolia*

Scuffledines. A popular grape in the Valley. The original scuppernong or mother vineyard is reported to be growing on Roanoke Island. The early explorers in the Valley spoke in great praise of the scuppernong. It is a whitish grape as contrasted with the muscadine or black grape. ʂ *Every year members of our community over the hill come when the grapes are odorous. "Mr. Green, could we pick a few scuffledines?"*

SCUPPERNONG GRAPES

TOP: SERVICEBERRY FLOWERS BOTTOM: SERVICEBERRY

SERVICEBERRY *Amelanchier arborea*
Sarviceberry, shadbush. How beautiful this tree is in the early spring when it adorns the woods with its foamy lacy blossoms. It grows into small-sized trees in all parts of the Valley. The berries are edible and have been used in stimulating beverages.

SHAGBARK HICKORY[13]
Carya carolinae-septentrionalis
A very fruitful hickory that grows especially in the upper reaches of the Valley. Sometimes they attain enormous size.

🐿️ *I have two on my farm that must be sixty or seventy feet tall and two feet or more in diameter near the base.*

SOUTHERN SHAGBARK HICKORY

SHEEP LAUREL FLOWERS

SHEEP LAUREL *Kalmia angustifolia*

This laurel grows in moist localities and in dry sandy acid soils and even bogs in North Carolina. The leaves and twigs and flowers of the shrub are narcotic and poisonous and have been used in the treatment of syphilis, scald-head and other skin infections. According to the word handed down, the Cree Indians used sheep laurel as a tonic and for bowel complaints.

SKUNK CABBAGE *Symplocarpus foetidus*

Polecat weed, swamp cabbage. This plant grows in swamps and low wet grounds in the Valley. The roots and tubers are supposed to be a narcotic and stimulant and, when dried or powdered, are a good remedy for asthma, catarrh, chronic coughs, dropsy, rheumatism and whatnot. Sometimes a salve made from the roots was used for ringworm and inflammatory rheumatism.

SLIPPERY ELM *Ulmus rubra*

Elm, ellum.

SPITBALLS

The dried bark of a slippery elm tree was used by baseball pitchers for throwing spitballs. When I was pitching sandlot ball in the Valley, I would buy the stuff at the drugstore in Angier to chew, and sometimes with the spittle just right and the motion just right, the ball would be sent toward the plate almost without turning. Then as it approached the plate it would dart downward and the batter usually missed it by a foot. But sometimes the slippery elm spittle would cause the ball to get away from me and a wild pitch would result. The spitball has been outlawed now in baseball.

SMARTWEED FLOWER SPIKE

SMARTWEED *Polygonum spp.*

Sometimes known as water pepper. It grows in the wet places throughout the Valley and even thrives in water itself. It has medicinal uses, being good for toothache, coughs, colds, milk sickness and even bowel complaints.

SMOOTH SUMAC

SMOOTH SUMAC *Rhus glabra*

This species of shrub grows in rocky or barren soils throughout the Valley and for that matter in almost all of North America. It is used as a cure for many diseases, claims being made it is good for gonorrhea, diarrhea, scrofula and fevers. The berries are supposed to be good for sore mouth and for gargling. In the case of burns, take equal parts of the beaten root mixed with equal parts of milk and water, thicken it with flour and apply it on freshly burned places, and, so the saying goes, not a scar will be left.

LEFT: SNAKEROOT   *RIGHT:* SNAKEROOT FLOWER

REMEDY FOR INFERTILITY

I know of one case where the man and his wife were married several years and snakeroot was recommended by an old neighbor. The man ate great quantities of it. His wife had twins born to her, and so they never got tired of recommending this to their friends.

In a play I once wrote called *The Founders*, my comedian married a woman who was barren and finding this remedy he took to snakeroot and ate a lot of it. "Till I fairly foamed at the mouth," he said. But the results were good, for his barren wife before many months had gone by presented him with twin sons, one of whom he named Thomas Dale after the governor and the other John Rolfe after Pocahontas' husband.

SNAKEROOT *Aristolochia serpentaria*

Sometimes called Sampson's snakeroot, pelican flower, or Virginia snakeroot. Tea made from this snakeroot is supposed to dry poison out of the body after a snakebite. It was recommended not only for snakebites but for high blood pressure and mental illness. It was supposed to have a tranquilizing effect. Some of the old people still recommend dry powdered leaves mixed with tobacco snuff and thickened into a paste with water as especially good for bee and wasp stings. There's a common belief that the Virginia variety, which also grows in the Valley, is especially good for increasing man's sexual powers.

❧ *Old Candiss McLean used to make a powder out of the root and snuff it up her nose to relieve her headache. She said it did her "a power of good." Perhaps it did for it is supposed to have the drug reserpine in it.*

61

SNEEZEWEED *Helenium autumnale*

Swamp sunflower. It grows abundantly in the Valley and according to some authorities the reason it is called "sneezeweed" is that if the leaves are dried and beaten into a powder and snuffed, they cause violent sneezing. The Indians were reported to have used it for snuffing up their noses. It is believed to be poisonous to cattle and sheep.

SOLOMON'S SEAL *Polygonatum biflorum*

A decorative little spring flower. The small blossoms which appear in April and May grow in clusters or singly on a flower stalk. The root chewed and swallowed was supposed to be a good cure for snakebites.

SNEEZEWEED

SOLOMON'S SEAL

SPANISH MOSS *Tillandsia usneoides*

A long moss[14] that grows in damp semitropical regions somewhat as a parasite. The lower part of the Valley is well stocked with it. It is referred to as "Old Graybeard." It especially seems to love pecan and live oak trees. I have seen orchards of the former down near the coast literally choked to death by it.

SPARROW GRASS *Asparagus officinalis*

Asparagus.

🦩 *I remember John Charles McNeill's poem which I memorized as a boy.*

"*I once et too much sparrow grass.*
They thought I was dead till I breathed on glass."

SPICEBUSH FLOWERS

SPICEBUSH *Lindera benzoin*

Fever bush, all spice. Attractive shrub that grows in the swamps and along the streams of the Valley. Oil from the berries of this bush is supposed to be good for bruises, white swelling, worms, pneumonia, colds, coughs, and especially it was good for these illnesses when mixed with sassafras tea. In the Civil War the soldiers who were camped in the Valley used this generally. The shrub seems to be getting rarer every year.[15]

TOP: SPRING BEAUTY   BOTTOM: SPRING BEAUTY FLOWERS

SPRING BEAUTY *Claytonia virginica*

A lovely wildflower that is popular among sweethearts in the Valley.

🦩 *I remember how in the spring a certain girl and I would go out in search especially of spring beauty. There was something so poetic in this little flower that it fitted right in with our yearnings and our mood, and it was innocent too. So that was good.*

TOP: SPRING GREEN AND GOLD BOTTOM: FLOWER HEAD DETAIL

SPRING GREEN AND GOLD

Chrysogonum virginianum
Green and gold. A low attractive perennial. It is one of the earliest blooming plants in the Valley. It grows especially in dry woodland and lasts on through the early summer.

STAGGERBUSH *Lyonia mariana*
A common shrub that grows in drier bogs and sand where the water table is shallow. It is poisonous and when stock, especially sheep, happen to eat of the leaves, they go staggering about. Therefore, the name.

STAR GRASS *Aletris farinosa*
Colic root. These little plants are found in the grassy woods in the deep summer. The plant grows abundantly in the woods and the bogs throughout the Valley. Tea made from the roots is supposed to be good for the colic.

STINGING NETTLE *Cnidoscolus stimulosus*
Tread-softly. The Indians were supposed to have counted these roots as a special delicacy, and the ancient Romans used them as a help against sexual impotency.

🐦 *We boys used to have great fun going out in the sandy woods and digging up stinging nettle roots. We could find them by their shiny white blossoms[16] here and there. Sometimes we would dig down two or three feet in the ground to find the tuber. These tubers were very succulent, and we had great fun eating them. They were usually about the size of a cigar and, much like a cigar, tapering at each end. We would peel them and chew the white delicious meat happily.*

■ *If you gently touch a nettle,*
  It will sting you for your pains.
  Grasp it like a man of mettle
  And as soft as silk remains.

■ *Out nettle, in dock,*
  Dock shall have a new smock.

STRAWBERRY BUSH IN FRUIT

STRAWBERRY BUSH *Euonymus americanus*

Hearts-a-busting-with-love, heart-bursting-with-love, swamp euonymus. A shrub that grows in moist places in the Valley and along the margins of watercourses. A decoction of the roots has been used for *prolapsus uteri* and also as a blood purifier.

SUGARBERRY *Celtis laevigata*

Hackberry. The fruit of the sugarberry tree eaten heavily was one of the many promising cures for syphilis. The Indians had faith in this practice as a cure after they'd caught the disease from the white man, or woman, but the berries didn't prevail.

SUGARBERRY TREE IN FRUIT

SUNFLOWER *Helianthus annuus*

The plant grows from the Arctic Circle to the tropics and is especially prolific in the Valley. The flowers are round, with petals yellow like the sun, but as to name, it is accounted for by the fact that, when in bloom, its "countenance" shows its adoration of the sun by turning toward it on its rising and turning with it as the hours proceed toward sunset. There are other and numerous uses for the plant—for chickenfeed, cure for dysentery and bladder infection and so on. The Indians used oil from the seed to grease their heavy hair. An old malaria cure was to have plenty of sunflowers growing about the house.

On cloudy days the sunflower's devotion to the sun is somewhat marred, though it does the best it can, however feebly. Thomas Moore, the Irish poet (1779-1852), has a lovely reference to this in his beautiful lyric, "Believe Me, If All Those Endearing Young Charms," set to an old Scotch melody.

> "The heart that has truly loved never forgets,
>   But as truly loves on to the close,
>   As the sunflower turns on her god when he sets
>   The same look which she turned when he rose."

SUNFLOWER

SWAMP DOGWOOD

SWAMP DOGWOOD *Cornus amomum*

Ague bark, water ash. A shrub found in the low moist woods and along the banks of the streams in the Valley. It is valuable as a cure for many diseases, and Burlage and Jacobs say that the Cree Indians used it for coughs and as a stimulant and a tonic. The bark was often used for a tonic and the chewed leaves aided in digestion. Its long stems were used to make baskets.

EASY PICKINGS

The dried seeds of the sunflower make wonderful bird feed. I have known the evening grosbeaks to be so greedy over the seed furnished in our bird feeder that their catalogued date of departure is delayed for weeks. They must have a pathological difficulty as to will to migrate, whatever the easy pickings – the welfare. But instinct always wins and they finally depart, and we look forward to next year when they can come again.

Sweet Bay

Swamp Mallow *Hibiscus moscheutos*
Marsh mallow. It grows in the borders of
marshes throughout the Valley. Seeds of this
swamp mallow make a good cordial and once
were used for acid stomach.

Sweet Bay *Magnolia virginiana*
One of the most decorated and beautiful trees
growing in the Valley. The sweet bay is seldom
found in the upper reaches of the Valley. The
leaves, the berries and the bark were good for
poulticing sores or swelling joints, and a tea
made from boiling the roots was used for children's colic. The tea was also good for gall-
stones, liver and spleen troubles in grown-ups.
The tree was supposed to have a mystic power
of protection in that neither witch nor devil,
thunder nor lightning would harm one where
sweet bay was planted.

❧ *I have got a couple planted near my house
in Chatham County close by Chapel Hill, but
I didn't plant them for fear of the witches, the
devil or thunder, but hoping to smell their sweet
blossoms. They have responded to that hope but
obviously with some effort.*

SWEET FLAG *Acorus calamus*

Calamus plant, calamus root. The root is supposed to be good for all sorts of stomach troubles. Tea from the boiled root was used to treat babies with colic.

TOO LATE FOR OLD MISS MINTY

I remember old Miss Minty who used to come and stay with us on a visit, how she would carry some of the sweet flag root wrapped up in her old handkerchief. And sometimes as she sat by the winter fire, she would take out the root in her trembling hands, break off a piece, put it in her toothless mouth, and sit there sucking it and staring peacefully at the fire. The root was supposed to be good for the preservation of the teeth and as an aphrodisiac, though too late to do old Miss Minty any good in either case.

SWEET FLAG

SWEET GUM TREE *Liquidambar styraciflua*

This tree grows prolifically in the Valley throughout its entire length and up into the edge of the mountains. The leaves of the tree are very aromatic and, if dried and beaten up and mixed with whiskey and taken regularly, were very good for irritable stomach. The dried balls of the tree with their little spikes were often used as decoration items on homemade furniture.

We children used to chop gashes in these trees and then later get the exuded gum and use it for chewing gum.

SWEET GUM, SHOWING MATURE AND IMMATURE "BALLS"

SWEET SHRUB *Calycanthus floridus*

Sweet Betsy. An odoriferous shrub. Carrying one of the buds in one's pocket was supposed to make the girls love you.

THISTLE *Carduus spp.*

A thorny field pest, a coarse biennial from two to three feet high. It grows from a thick taproot and its spiny leaves, especially when dried, can be a torment to bare feet. There are some seven species in the Valley. It grows everywhere it gets

SWEET SHRUB FLOWERS

a chance to grow and has one redeeming feature —beautiful reddish purple flowers. When the root is boiled in milk it is supposed to be good for the dysentery. According to a folklore pharmacist friend of mine, a salve or even a tincture from it was once supposed to be good for eczema and other skin irritations.

A TONGUE-TWISTER

Theophilis Thistle, the thistle sifter,
Sifted a sack of thistles with the thick of his thumb.
A sack of thistles did Theophilis Thistle,
    the thistle sifter, sift.

If Theophilis Thistle, the thistle sifter,
Sifted a sack of thistles with the thick of his thumb,
Where is the sack of thistles that
    Theophilis Thistle sifted?

THISTLE

TICKLE TAIL *Setaria spp.*

A gossamer-like weed.

🌿 *We children used to gather these tickle tails in handfuls where they had wind-drifted into fence jambs and tickle our noses to make ourselves sneeze.*

TICKWEED *Bidens polylepis*

Smooth tickseed. A lovely little sunflower which gladdens the roadsides in summer. Its leaves help as an expectorant.

TOAD-FLAX *Linaria spp.*

A common Valley wildflower but uncommon in that some species are annual and biennial as well as perennial. One species bears showy yellow flowers, grows from one to three feet tall, and is a good spectacle along ditches and in muddy places in spring and early summer. Another species is called blue toad-flax as contrasted with yellow toad-flax[17] and often turns old fields blue with its azure beauty.

TICKWEED

LEFT: TOAD-FLAX FLOWERS *RIGHT:* FIELD OF TOAD-FLAX NEAR PAUL GREEN'S BIRTHPLACE

It is poisonous to cattle. A tincture was sometimes used for jaundice and externally for hemorrhoids.

TOOTHACHE TREE *Aralia spinosa*
Devil's walking stick, Hercules' club, Mexican mulberry, pigeon tree, prickly ash, shot bush, spikenard tree. A thorny tree or shrub known by a number of names. The fresh bark of this tree is an emetic and cathartic and is also reputed to be an antidote for the bite of the rattlesnake. Other recommendations for it say it is good for cholera, rheumatism, syphilis and of course toothache as well as the dropsy. The oil of the seed of this tree has been used in earache and deafness and for all sorts of rheumatic pains.

🦫 *It grew in abundance on the plantation of my great-great-great grandfather, Colonel Alexander McAllister. A couple of years ago poking around the woods of the old place, I found a grove of these gnarled and awkward trees. I dug up two or three small ones and took them to Chapel Hill and planted them in our wildflower garden and there they are flourishing well. I think of old Colonel Alexander McAllister every time I see them.*

TOOTHACHE TREE IN FRUIT

71

TOUCH-ME-NOT *Impatiens capensis*

Jewel weed. This plant grows in damp shady places from eastern Canada to Florida and was often used in dysentery and kidney troubles. The flowers sometimes were crushed into a watery pulp and used for dyeing.

TOUCH-ME-NOT

TRAILING ARBUTUS *Epigaea repens*

Arbutus, ground laurel. An early spring creeping plant with very delicate and much admired little flowers. It grows from Michigan to Florida and best on the north side of the Valley hills. A tincture of the plant was once used for kidney trouble, so the herb artists say.

How many miles have my wife and I tramped the woods searching for this shy and heavenly sweet "ground laurel." We once found a colony of it just north of old Barbecue Church near the spring where Flora MacDonald and her stalwart husband Allen used to worship and listen to Reverend John McLeod's sermons in both Gaelic and English. My wife and I have transplanted specimens of it several times to our Chatham County farm but have had poor success with it.

TRAILING ARBUTUS

TRUMPET VINE FLOWERS

TRUMPET VINE *Campis radicans*

Cow itch vine. This plant was and still is possessed of a bad name in the Valley, for it's supposed to be especially poisonous to children's skin, almost as bad as poison ivy.

IT KNOWS WHERE IT'S GOING

I used to play around a trumpet vine and climb up it when I was a child but never was hurt by it. There's one thing about the vine though I've noticed in more recent years, and that is it seems to be a thing almost of instinct. It will climb right on up to the top of the highest tree before it begins sending out its branches. I wonder how it knows when it's got to where it's going. But there are plenty of plants and things in the Valley that seem to have this fore-knowledge, for instance, the Venus' fly trap, the be-shame bush (sensitive plant), aspen tree and others.

TRUMPET VINE

73

DAVIE POPLAR ON CAMPUS OF UNC-CHAPEL HILL

TULIP TREE *Liriodendron tulipifera*

Yellow poplar. This large timber tree is common in rich soil throughout the United States. It is especially plentiful in the Valley. There is a tulip tree, known as the Davie Poplar, which is a rather sacrosanct object on the campus of the University of North Carolina at Chapel Hill. It was under this tree that General William R. Davie took lunch in 1789 when he and his committee chose the site for the university. Yellow poplar timber is especially good for veneering since it takes a higher polish than any other American wood.

TULIP TREE FLOWER

TURKEY CALLER

A device for imitating the call of a turkey. Cousin Hardy Draughan of Dunn invented one consisting of a little resonant poplar wood box with a thin wooden lip against which he would scrape a piece of slate; the result was a sound exactly like a call of a turkey. He sold this contraption to Sears and Roebuck for a goodly sum, and I used to see it advertised in the catalog.

TURK'S-CAP LILY

TURK'S-CAP LILY[18] *Lilium michauxii*

One of the most beautiful of all lilies, gorgeous with its Turk's cap. It's a sacrilege to say with the pharmacists that a tincture of the fresh bulb will cause constipation, mouth-burning and restlessness.

🐢 *Last summer when my wife and I were walking in the deep oak woods east of our house, I saw a spot of gold shining low in a little opening off to the left. We ran there and stood in awe over the little lovely creature, alone, perfect. We will watch for it next summer.*

TURTLEHEAD *Chelone glabra*

Another name is chelone and still another, fish-mouth or snake-mouth. The flowers of this perennial herb resemble the head of a turtle,

and therefore its name. A tonic made from its leaves is supposed to be a good treatment for worms. And it is said that the Indians used it as a tonic and laxative.

TURTLEHEAD

TWIN BLUEBELL *Ruellia caroliniensis*

Hairy ruellia, ruellia. A fine little plant common in the dry woods throughout the Valley and good to have in a wildflower garden. Its name is rightly descriptive. So far as I know, it is an exception in that it has no medicinal value.

VANILLA PLANT *Trillisa odoratissima*

A plant from eighteen inches to four feet in height with numerous heads of purplish and sometimes white flowers in a terminal cluster. It grows in grassy bog areas all through the Valley and in the old days, so they say, was used as an adulterant in tobacco. Tea made from the aromatic leaves is a good stimulant. Also cuttings from the plant were once used in closets as protection against moths.

VENUS' FLY TRAP *Dionaea muscipula*

Flytrap. This is certainly one of the world's most unique plants. The two-lobed leaf of these small

TWIN BLUEBELL

perennials is red inside and attracts insects which light to enjoy the spread-out viand. The lobes, about an inch or more long, suddenly close over their quarry and devour it by absorption. The eating done, they open again and offer their apparently innocent food to the needy.

🌿 *This plant used to be prolific in the lower part of the Valley. A few years ago one could see it for sale on the streets of Chapel Hill. It is now protected by law.*

VENUS' FLY TRAP *LEFT: LEAVES RIGHT: FLOWER BUDS*

VENUS' LOOKING-GLASS *Specularia perfoliata*
A slender erect little annual from one-half to
two feet high with purple flowers. It blossoms
from late April through August. It actually is
not a flower but a little weed and is often a pest
in a vegetable garden. So far as I know, it has no
medicinal value.

TOP: BIRD'S FOOT VIOLET   *BOTTOM:* HALBERD-LEAVED VIOLET

VETCH

VETCH *Vicia spp.*
A common trailing vine that grows throughout
the Valley and is found especially in grain fields.
Some people identify it with the tare spoken
of in the Bible. The seeds are detergent and,
according to the old horse and cow doctors, it
causes the bloat in animals and also is injurious
to swine.

VIOLET *Viola spp.*
One of the most popular little flowers on earth.
There are some sixteen different kinds of violets
that grow in the Valley, running from the beard-
ed white violet through the early blue and on
down to the tri-lobed leafed yellow violet. This
flower has been praised by musicians and poets
through the ages. A poultice made from the
roots of the common "blue" violet is a good
remedy for bone felons and boils.

🌿 *One of our happiest experiences when we
were children was to go into the woods in the
early spring, especially where the land had been
burnt over, and gather great handfuls of violets
and bury our noses in them deliciously.*

VIPER'S BUGLOSS *Echium vulgare*

Sometimes called blue-weed, it is found in dry meadows and pastures in the central and northern part of the Valley. The root contains a poisonous alkaloid which produces eruptions and irritations of the skin.

VIRGINIA CREEPER

VIRGINIA CREEPER *Parthenocissus quinquefolia*

American ivy. It is a strong climbing vine common in the woods through the Valley. This plant is popular for use in decorating chimneys and shares its popularity only with the English ivy.

VIRGINIA DAY FLOWER *Commelina virginica*

A beautiful and delicate plant which flowers in July and grows in either moist or medium dry soil. According to my friend Burlage, it is a good relaxant and works well on constipation.

Not long ago my wife and I discovered two of these plants growing along the edge of the little stream that flows from our spring back of the house. Nearly every day in walking along our path we would turn off to see these little flowers.

VIRGINIA DAY FLOWER

VIRGIN'S BOWER *Clematis virginiana*

Clematis, Virginia virgin's bower. It grows in wet waste places and in the thickets and borders of woods and is found throughout the Valley. It has been reported to be useful in the treatment of syphilitic eruptions, skin diseases and itch— diseases coarsely antagonistic to its gentle name.

VIRGIN'S BOWER

WAKE-ROBIN

VOMITWORT *Lobelia inflata*

Vomitweed, pukeweed, Indian tobacco, wild
tobacco, tobacco lobelia, groot. This herb grows
in fields and along roadsides in the upper part
of the Valley. It is supposed to be good for
dozens of ailments such as whooping cough,
hernia, headache, tremors, nausea and vomiting.
It has also been used in the treatment of epilepsy,
pneumonia, hysteria, cramps and convulsions.
It is poisonous to animals and therefore in their
good sense they let it alone. And now, with all
the new vitamin pills and mycin drugs, man is
letting the plant alone also.

WAKE-ROBIN[19] *Trillium cuneatum*

Birthroot, bumblebee-root, Daffydown Dilly,
ground lily, Indian shamrock, red Benjamin,
trillium. Although its name refers to the waking
of the robins, the plant comes to leaf usually
long after the robins have already waked up and
gone on their way north. This bulbous plant
grows in rich shady woodland soils and goes by
a dozen or more different names. The roots of
the wake-robin are astringent and tonic.

■ *"Daffydown Dilly has now come to town*
   In a red petticoat and a green gown."

WALNUTS

WALNUT *Juglans nigra*

Warnit, black walnut. A large-growing and valuable timber tree which grows in rich soils in all parts of the Valley. It is especially prized for the making of cabinets and other furniture. Walnut bark and leaves have many good medicinal uses. The leaves are moderately aromatic, bitter and astringent, and the inner bark of the tree and the root are mild cathartics, acting, so it is said, "on the bowels without pain and debilitating the alimentary tract." A salve made from the leaves was supposed to be a sure cure for leg sores.

A common nut in the Valley, a hard shell as opposed to the softer-shelled English walnut. The goodies inside the hard shells are highly esteemed. Machinery has been invented now to crack the walnuts and get the goodies out without mashing them.

The Indians in the Valley used the rind of the green fruit in staining and dyeing. Juice from a green walnut hull was most efficacious in the treatment of ringworm, ring-around, poison ivy, or skin eruptions and diseases, provided the victim could endure the burning pain caused by the juice.

Our daughter had some walnut boards which were cut from our farm shipped to Boston, and Frank Hubbard made her a beautiful harpsichord out of them. She performs on it most happily.

WATERCRESS *Nasturtium officinale*
A cress that grows in wet boggy places, even in standing water, and is highly prized as a vegetable and salad in early spring. It is supposed also to be a good tonic and blood purifier for children.

WATER HEMLOCK *Cicuta maculata*
This plant is sometimes called death of man, or wild parsnip. It grows in all parts of the Valley, in swamps and in wet low-grounds. The plant is acrid and narcotic and the fresh roots are supposed to be especially toxic.

WATER LILY *Nymphaea spp.*
A decorative lily now used in many flower garden pools. There are several kinds of water lilies.

WATER LILY

WHITE ALDER

WHITE ALDER[20] *Clethra alnifolia*
Pepperbush, sweet pepperbush. This species grows in swamps and damp places from Maine to Florida and throughout North Carolina. Tea made from it was once a good medicine for fevers, coughs and lung afflictions.

WHITE MULBERRY *Morus alba*
Silkworm tree. This tree is a native of China and has been naturalized in the Valley. Back in the old, old days it was thought that silkworms could be raised and fed on the leaves of these trees and the manufacture of silk would result. But just as up in Virginia, the experiment failed. The root of the tree is astringent, and a tea made from its bark is supposed to be good for diarrhea.

White Oak on campus of UNC-Chapel Hill

White Oak *Quercus alba*

Perhaps the most beautiful of all trees in the Valley. For a long while it has been the main source of cross ties for the railroads, in ship-building, flooring, framing, and a multitude of other uses. The acorns have been good for fattening hogs and the bark is astringent, used in tanning and for all sorts of medicinal purposes, gargles and injections. White oak strips were much used for making baskets and chair bottoms especially.

Farm objects made from white oak withes:
- *Corn basket: a basket for handling corn in the ear.*
- *Cotton basket: a basket used to pour the picked cotton in for weighing or for emptying into the wagon body.*
- *Muzzle: an old-timey contrivance used over the mouth of a mule, a horse, or a steer so that the animal wouldn't eat the corn or cotton while plowing.*

Wild Ginger *Hexastylis arifolia*

Heartleaf or little pigs. An aromatic Valley plant, the early leaves resembling small pigs' ears. Poultices from the leaves are used to heal cuts.

Melinda Chapin's Children

Pellagra and hookworm diseases years ago were for a long while Yankee-given attributes to the Old South, and then came Franklin D. Roosevelt's description, "economic problem number one." But that is all changed. The South is now perhaps the healthiest place in the country, and since the "sun belt" craze has struck, it is the fastest growing.

But all has come a little late for, say, Melinda Chapin and her five illegitimate children. This family lived in our neighborhood, and in addition to having the shame of bastardy on them, they were afflicted with hookworm. And they were filthy and stank more than a hot compost heap. You could smell them almost before you could see them. The welfare lady kept sending them to the hospital in Fayetteville where they'd be treated for awhile, and then they'd come home no better than when they left. Finally "Doctor" Cicero East made up a tea from the wild ginger and pipsissewa plants and fed it to them by the quart. They recovered from their hookworm, but he never did get them so they didn't stink.

WILD INDIGO *Baptisia tinctoria*

Fly killer, horsefly killer, horsefly weed. This plant is found in fertile soils from Virginia to Florida, and is usually two to four feet high. It had its medicinal uses too in the old days. One ounce of boiled root to one pint of hot water made a good tonic. Dose—one teaspoonful every three or four hours.

🐾 *We used to fasten sprigs of it in the mules' bridles to keep the flies away.*

WILD INDIGO FLOWERS

TOP: WILD GINGER IN FLOWER *BOTTOM:* WILD GINGER, EARLY LEAVES

WILD IRIS EMERGING THROUGH WATER LILY LEAVES

WILD IRIS *Iris virginica*
A beautiful small iris that grows in damp places and even in wet swamps. The root is chewed or eaten for numerous complaints, dropsy, spleen and kidney afflictions, and as a good purgative.

WILD ONION *Allium canadense*
Ramps.[21] A common pest throughout the Valley. The juice or syrup from its bulbs has been used for colic in infants.

WILD POTATO VINE *Ipomoea pandurata*
Another curse to the farmer. It grows prolifically in very poor soil and its roots go down beyond the reach of a plow. Its tubers were once used by the Valley Indians for food.

WILD STRAWBERRY *Fragaria virginiana*
A smaller strawberry than the garden variety but an exquisite fruit for jam and also a good remedy, so it is said, for gout.

WILD STRAWBERRY

WITCH GRASS *Leptoloma cognatum*

Couch grass or dog grass. A pest hard to get rid of. It is found in the fields and waste places in the Valley, and a drink from it was once used for irritations of the bladder and kidney diseases.

WITCH HAZEL FLOWERS

WITCH HAZEL *Hamamelis virginiana*

Hazel, spotted alder. It is a sort of tree-like shrub and has the distinction of blooming in December like the wintersweet. The tea from witch hazel taken by the expectant mother was supposed to be an aid to childbirth.

❧ *Many people in the Valley in the old days would keep a green hazel stick stuck up over the door of the house where a baby was expected. This was supposed to keep off witches and any evil influences.*

WOOD SORREL *Oxalis violacea*

Oxalis, sheep sorrel, sorrel, sour clover. It grows in the Valley damp places and is a diuretic. Old Mis' Zua Smith used to beat up the plant and mix it with butter or some sort of grease and use it to cure sores on people's lips.

DOWSING RODS

Forked witch hazel twigs were used in the old days, and now and then you find a person who still uses them as diviners' or dowsing rods in locating good places to dig wells for water or hunt for hidden treasure.

I remember the Negro well-digger and mason, Uncle Lawrence Askew, going about with his witch hazel twig, a forked twig. Holding it before him with both hands, he'd tramp around till he felt it turning in his hands, and then he would say, "Right here's the place to dig and you'll get a good well of water."

I talked to Uncle Lawrence about it. "Do you mean it really turned in your hand, Uncle Lawrence?"

"It sho' did. You might put all your man to it and try to hold it to keep it from turning, but it would turn just the same. It felt the power of the water down below pulling on it, yes sir."

WOOD SORREL

TOP: YARROW FLOWER HEADS   *BOTTOM:* YARROW

YARROW *Achillea millefolium*

Dog daisy, old man's pepper. This plant grows in dry pasture places. It was supposed to be used by Achilles and his name is often given to it. The flowers and leaves make a good tea and the Indians used to take it for stomach trouble.

YAUPON *Ilex vomitoria*

Yaupon holly, Carolina tea. This is a tree shrub that grows in the lower part of the Valley. The Indians made a sort of black drink from it, and some of the people in the Valley still make yaupon tea.

Not so long ago I attended a yaupon party given by Mrs. Winslow. Some yaupon drink had been made from the dry leaves and one cup of that stuff was enough to last me quite a while, but some of the guests drank it and praised it highly. They can have it.

YAUPON, SHOWING FLOWERS AND PREVIOUS SEASON'S BERRIES

YELLOW JESSAMINE

YELLOW JESSAMINE *Gelsemium sempervirens*
A prolific vine, loaded with yellow flowers. It is becoming popular as a vine to decorate porches or fences.

YELLOWROOT *Xanthorhiza simplicissima*
This plant grows mainly in the upper Piedmont and in the mountains. Tea is made from it and is supposed to be good for the sore throat or thrash and also for nerves.

YELLOWROOT IN FLOWER

YUCCA

YUCCA *Yucca filamentosa*

Adam's needle, Adam's needle and thread, bear grass, Christmas bells, silk grass, Spanish bayonet, Spanish needles. This plant is becoming more and more popular in the Valley because of its gorgeous column of creamy white flowers. The tincture of the root was once used for rheumatism and gonorrhea, and, it is said, the Indian doctors used a salve made from it for inflammation. A strong tea made from it was always a good gargle for the sore throat.

YUCCA FLOWERS

MORE TALES
& PLANT LORE

from
PAUL GREEN'S
WORDBOOK

200-YEAR OLD PERSIMMON TREE, ON THE CAMPUS OF UNC-CHAPEL HILL

THE GHOST IN THE TREE

GHOST: *A spirit of a dead person appearing on earth again,*
such as Hamlet's father's ghost. Often referred to as ha'nt.

GHOST STORIES ARE UNIVERSALLY POPULAR and how often we children shivered with delight as we listened to one. The more pitiful or scary, the better—such as the following. I've heard several versions of this story, all differing in particulars but agreeing on the fact of the ha'nt. This one I got from an old local historian, Jim Fallon. I allowed for his imagination.

"Well, a long time ago when the Yankees were fighting with the Southern folk," said Old Jim, as we sat by his fire one night, "General Sherman and his soldiers ravaged through the country burning and destroying things. They crossed the Cape Fear at Fayetteville which they burnt and went all around seizing up provisions and victuals—what they could find. They come on up the river into our neighborhood— some of 'em did. And a company of 'em put up in Squire Barclay's big grove.

"The Squire had a great big house too, but they said they'd put up their tents out-doors and sleep in them like always if he didn't mind. They seemed mighty polite, and he said go right ahead. And I reckon they'd a-done it anyhow, whether or why, for I've always heard them Yankee soldiers were mighty rough, and certain they were, as I'll tell you.

"Now the Squire and his wife had a little boy, and he was much took with the soldiers and the rifles and clamping swords and bayonets and he kept brushing around and asking questions and telling 'em no doubt about what old Sandy Claus had brung him for Christmas. The Squire done what he could for the soldiers when suppertime come. He had his slave women bring out what beef and sweet potatoes he could fur-nish and some cider and peach brandy—not much but some. Them soldiers et and drunk and felt purty good no doubt and thought the Southerners maybe were not so bad after all. Later some of 'em poking about found a big cask of scuppernong wine in the barn where the Squire had it hid away in the shucks. They went after that hot and heavy, and soon they were feeling more than fine. They were getting drunk.

"Now the Squire and his wife had done gone to sleep in the big house, and the little boy was supposed to be asleep too. The captain of the soldiers had told the Squire that he would see that nothing was disturbed and he and his men would take care of everything. I reckon after all the Yankees were not so bad, though I heard old Miz Nancy Demming say once that her daddy saw one of 'em squatted behind his barn, his britches down and him doing his natural business and he had a long tail like the devil hisself. And I've heard other old folks say that some of 'em had hoofs too.

"Well, that little boy couldn't sleep for thinking about the soldiers and their blue coats and their swo'ds and everything, and so he laid in his little bed listening to the happenings down in the grove, some talking and singing maybe. And when everybody else in the house was quiet, he got up and croped out and went down there. And there set the soldiers all full of liquor and a-jawing with one another.

"And some of 'em was cussing now and about to fight. When the boy come up to 'em they all stopped and looked at him, and one of them said, 'Sonny, you better be in bed.'

"Nother'n said, 'Let him set up—'twon't hurt him.'

"Then they all got to asking questions and bragging on him and said, 'Your father's a big rich man, he must have horses and plenty of silver and things buried in the ground.'

"'If Father did have horses and such hid away I wouldn't tell you,' the boy said.

"'What's that?' said the big captain of a soldier who was drunk with the rest of 'em by this time.

"'I wouldn't tell you,' said the boy.

"'Well, maybe he has,' said the captain, 'and was lying when he told us everything's been sent to the Confederate Army—horses, money, and everything.'

"'I ain't going to tell you,' said the boy, 'and you better quit calling my father a liar.'

"And then they got to fooling with him, half joking and half serious.

"'If you don't tell us, we might hang you up high as Haman.'

"Of course they didn't mean it—they was just joking and picking at him. But he begun to cry and you know how it is sometimes when anybody cries. It's liable to make you meaner than you was, if you're set on pestering of 'em. And that's the way it was with them. They didn't give way to feeling sorry for him.

"'Shut up,' they said, and then they begun to give him some minny balls and one of 'em give him a piece of new money with a picture on it, and he hushed his crying. They begun to pick at him again, asking him about all them horses and where that silver and money was buried, 'cause they had already got the idea from the way he acted that that little boy knowed something. And he might for all I know.

"Of course, they didn't mean no harm maybe but they were getting good drunk by this time. And you know how it is when folks get drunk and a long ways from home—from their women-folks at home—they are just like as not to get powerful mean.

"And then the big captain soldier said, 'By God, we'll hang the little rascal on that limb if he don't tell.'

"And another said, 'By God, we will.' But you know—that little fellow wouldn't tell a word, nary'n.

"And one of the soldiers tied a handkerchief around his little mouth so he couldn't squeal much. Lord, I wished I had been off in the barn with a rifle or up on a rooftop some'r's.

"There was a big 'simmon tree there in the grove with the limbs spread out and a little swing on it where the little boy used to swing. And one of the soldiers took his sword and cut the rope in two. Then they tied it around the little boy under the armpits and hung him up.

" 'Now,' they said, 'you going to tell us about them horses and where that there money's hid,' and the little boy kept shaking his head.

" 'You gonna tell,' they said. And he kept shaking his head.

"Golly, that little young'un was a stout Trojas man all right. Then they started swinging him back and forth, way here and way there until his head would almost touch the limbs of the red oaks beyond. And he couldn't make nary a sound 'cause they had his mouth covered up with that handkerchief, and his hands tied.

"When he would swing by him, the big soldier would say, 'You gonna tell?' And the little boy would shake his head.

"Then the big soldier got bull mad, and he shouted out so loud that he roused the Squire up in his bed where he slept. 'You gonna tell me? I ask you for the last time!'

"And the little boy shook his head, and then as he swung back towards him, that there soldier pulled out his sword and run it through the little boy's stomach and killed him—unh!

"Well, the Squire and his wife had come out on the porch, 'cause they had heard the loud shouting. They went rushing down towards the soldiers, the two of 'em in their white nightgowns and throwing up their hands. And when they seen the little boy hanging there by the firelight, his head bent over like Jesus on the cross and blood drip-drapping from him to the ground, they both went wild and run at the soldiers clawing and scratching like cats. And the soldiers killed both of 'em, so 'twas said. And the big soldier stood there drunk swinging the little boy, all the time swinging him back and forth, and all of a sudden he gave the little body such a swing that it swung high up and lodged in the fork of the 'simmon tree.

"Then when they'd done so much damage—killed the boy and Squire and his wife, 'cause they was all so drunk, they set fire to the house. And the black folks run all out of their cabins into the fields, hollering and screaming while the house burned down. The soldiers shot some of them just to see them fall, so 'twas said. Then they packed up their stuff, saddled their horses and got away from there as fast as they could, and they never more did come back.

"Later the white folks cleaned up that grove and made a field of it, but they didn't touch that 'simmon tree. You know how it is, they leave 'simmon trees down in fields, the way it is in my field down there. And one night when I was about yearling size, I went with my daddy coon-hunting over on the hill there. We had four dogs named Rang, Gouge, Buster and Bo-Peep, and they were the best coon dogs that ever there was.

"Well, we hadn't been out hunting more'n a few minutes when we up and struck a hot track, and they run up and down the swamps—'Yow-yow-yow,' as hard as life would let 'em. Then out on the hills and back again, they'd come. There was something quare about it, 'cause a coon don't usually run like that. He sticks straight in the swamp. Then the dogs struck a trail out of the swamp again—'Yow-yow-yow,' up the hill, across the field toward where the old Barclay house had been, and all of a sudden the racket stopped.

" 'What do you reckon's happened now?' I said, and my daddy said they must have ketched him. Then he said they couldn't a-ketched him, and if the coon had gone up the tree they couldn't have clambed the tree to get at him there.

"Whilst we stood in the edge of the field a-talking it over, here come the dogs back as hard as life would let 'em run. And they got quite clost up to us and whined and whimpered.

" 'That ain't no coon,' said my daddy.

" 'What is it?' I said. And he didn't know he said, but it weren't no coon. And we'd try him again, he said.

"Now them dogs was well trained, and when my daddy spoke, they knowed what to do. Everybody did, when he spoke.

" 'Get on there, Rang, get on, Gouge, you, Buster and you, Bo-Peep.'

"And he set 'em off again—'yow, yow, yow.' They run the trail on across the old field and towards where the old house had been and where that 'simmon tree stood up plain in the moonlight. Purty soon there they come back lickity-lick, lickity-lick. And they croped up around and hugged up close to our legs, whimpering and a-whining.

" 'It ain't no coon,' my daddy says.

" 'What is it?' I say.

" 'You know what it is?' he says. And I say I don't.

"And he says, 'It's a ha'nt—if what I heard as a boy is so, but I ain't never seen a ha'nt in my life, and maybe tonight's a good time to see one.'

"Of course he was half joking-like, for he really didn't believe all he'd heard about the old Barclay place, and I didn't neither—little as I was.

"Now my daddy weren't a-scared of nothing dead or alive. So he says, 'We're going to see. Here, Rang, here Buster,' and we started out acrost the fields.

"But you know them dogs wouldn't run nary another step. They come slipping behind, and every once in a while they'd let out a pitiful wheeah-wheeah sound. Purty soon we come up to that old 'simmon tree and there in the moonlight you could see something a-setting in it. Great God, something bigger'n a 'possum was a-setting in it. There weren't no bears in the country, not even no wolves, and I begun to feel funny.

" 'Come on,' said my daddy, and he went on up with me behind—and Rang and Gouge and Buster and Bo-Peep all in a row.

"Well, we come a little closer and there, bless God, up in the 'simmon tree shining in the moonlight was that little boy or something that looked like a boy.

"I stood froze in my tracks. But my daddy sure had a craw full o' grit, and he said he was going to climb that 'simmon tree and get that little boy or whatever it was, and if it was flesh and blood he'd take him home and raise him.

"I begged him not to try, but he did. And he climbed on up that 'simmon tree and got right close to where that critter was sitting. And then it run out along the limb to the clean tip of it and hung there by one hand like a 'possum, and my daddy shook the limb so hard that it fell off way down to the ground and hit the ground running—and away it went as hard as its little legs could carry it toward the graveyard back of where the old house has been.

"But the dogs didn't go after him, no sir. They set right there and whined and whined. And when my daddy come down, he was white as a sheet.

" 'What's the matter?' I said.

" 'Come on,' he said, 'let's get away from here.'

"Both of us and the dogs left as hard as life would let us. And my daddy said that little boy or whatever it was had breathed in his face.

"Other people seen him in that 'simmon tree too, and it got so nobody would go nigh that place. The briar-bushes growed up about the tree, and the field got full of sassafras scrubs, and the last time I was around there it was full of pines and young sweet gums and new dogwoods. And there'll never more be a plow stuck in it till the end of time. That's what I reckon."

SOAPMAKING

IN THE OLD DAYS the Valley housewife made her own soap. I remember my mother used to make soap in the same big iron pot we used for heating water for hog-killing. She would put in a lot of the trimmings of the pork and boiled pieces of meat of all sorts, have a fire built around the pot and, after cooking these for a good long while, add lye and other ingredients. Then after it had boiled down to a rather thick soupy mixture she would let the fire die out and the ingredients cool and the soap harden.

The next day Mother would take a kitchen knife and cut the hardened mass into cakes. Now we had soap enough to last for months and we used it for all sorts of cleanings. How pleased we were when we would get a piece of store-bought soap in place of old homemade stuff.

There are many beliefs connected with soapmaking, among them the following:

If homemade soap is to be solid, only one person must stir it and always in the same direction. To reverse the stroke of the stirring stick is to prevent the solution from congealing no matter how long it cooks or what additional ingredients are put in it.

A sassafras stick should be used for stirring and always in one direction.

Another belief is to stir as the sun turns. Otherwise the ingredients will not mix and the soap will not do well. The same was thought to be true of cake batter.

If you make soap while the moon is waning, the soap will dry up. So make soap on the increase of the moon.

Others say that the fat meat and lye will come to the proper congealing in the full of the moon.

If a man calls on you while you are making soap, get him to stir the soap ingredients and it will improve the quality.

It is bad luck for a woman to call on you while you are making soap. The same is not true of a man.

I found an old recipe for homemade soap as follows—a proper mixture of hickory ashes, lye, grease, skins, pieces of fat sidemeat, hog ears, the feet, and so on. Boil and keep boiling until they are completely dissolved, and then let the mixture cool off and you will have good soap.

THE UNIVERSITY GENTLEMEN

I'VE KNOWN DOWSERS who claimed that a peach tree fork or even dogwood would work just as well as witch hazel. And some more scientific ones now say that metal rods held before the dowser as he walks will do the trick too.

Recently I looked out through the window of my work cabin and saw a man moving back and forth in the meadow with two little rods extended in front of him. A service truck with the big insignia of the University of North Carolina (*Lux et Libertas*) on its side stood nearby, and two other men were standing leaning against it. Curious, I left off working on my *Cross and Sword* play and went out and asked the gentleman what he was up to—if he didn't mind saying. He said he was locating a water line. In his hands he held two little brass rods sticking far out at right angles from his hands and free to swivel in the small metal collar pieces he grasped.

"When these rods start cutting up, I will be near the pipe," he said.

"You mean they will tell you where it is?" I asked somewhat incredulously.

"Sure do," he said. "And when I get right over the pipe, the rods will cross themselves one over the other in front of me and stay crossed. Yes, sir."

"Wonderful," I said. But I didn't believe it, for just the night before I had been reading a lot of stuff Joseph Wood Krutch had written about the New England dowsers. I stood around quite a while watching this representative of the University trying to find the pipe.

"Doesn't the University have a survey that shows where it has laid its pipelines?" I asked.

"Not this one," he said. "It's a private line to your house anyhow and hooks up to the main line yonder in the Raleigh Road."

"Yes, but the University put it in. Maybe you did," I said, "though I paid for it."

"I might have," he said, "but I've put in so many I can't remember them all." He kept walking around to no avail, and I began mentally to estimate the cost he and his truck and the two fellows were penalizing the taxpayers.

Seeing at last that he wasn't making any progress, I told him I knew where the water line was, and so I showed him.

"I remember the day it was put in," I said, "and it went along near this pine here, first to my cabin and then on by it to the house." The information didn't seem to matter to him one way or the other.

"I would a-found it afterwhile anyhow," he said. "These rods never fail me. Now if it's terra cotta pipe, that's another thing. Clay don't seem to attract them, but metal does. When I walk in the woods, for instance, say, on Sunday, I carry a pair of these with me—not just these two, for they belong to the University Buildings Department, but two like them. You never know when you might be walking over metal or even silver or gold in the ground," he said.

"Will they find silver and gold too?" I queried.

"I'm sure they will," he said.

"I wonder if I could get me a set of these rods?" I asked.

"Sure thing," he said, "just phone Mr. Branch at the Buildings Department and he'll fix you up." He now called out to the two men at the truck, "Heigh, fellows, bring your shovels, Mr. Paul says this is where we'll have to dig."

The next day I called up Mr. Branch and for two dollars he ordered me a set of rods. I now keep them on my wall to look at and, I guess, to remind me that all of us are folklorists and filled with folk customs and superstitions from the cradle to the grave. I had first tried them out before I laid them up.

Sometime after this, two scientists from the Massachusetts Institute of Technology were visiting us. I told them about the rods and showed them to them. When I started to replace them on the mantel, one of the scientists took them again in his hand and felt them. Then I saw "that look" come into his eyes.

"I believe I'll go out and try them," he said. We went outside and for a good while he too wandered up and down the meadow holding them extended in front of him. Presently he came back and handed them to me.

"There's nothing to it, of course," he said.

The other scientist laughed a bit jeeringly. "I mark that 'of course,'" he said.

"Then why did you try them?"

"Just a prank," the other one said.

As we started back to the house, the second scientist said, "Wait a minute, I believe I'll try those things too."

I handed him the rods.

CANCER CURE

"WHEN I WAS A YOUNG MAN," said Mr. Mac, as we sat in his millhouse one night while he caught up on his late corn-grinding, "there was an old woman lived in the Rockfish neighborhood named Miss Zua Smith. She was supposed to be one of the best herb doctors in the whole Cape Fear Valley, and she claimed to have discovered a cure for cancer. Maybe she did. Anyway she used to make tumor or cancer plasters and sell them for fifty cents apiece.

"A few miles off from her near my daddy's place lived old Archie Norwood, who had a cancer on the side of his face. Doctor John McKay, the father of Dr. Joe, treated him as best he could and said he ought to go to a hospital or somewhere and git it burned off. And even that might do no good, for it was a bad one, mighty bad. But Archie wouldn't go. He went down instead to Miss Zua and got one of her plasters and put it on his face. And when the strength would go out of that he would go get another. I'm a witness to the fact that he was cured. I've seen him at church many a time, and only a little scar showed where the terrible affliction once had been.

"There are many other old folks walking or riding the highways of the Valley who can testify to the fact of her cures. She would take sorrel, beat the juice out of it on a pewter plate, put it in the sun until it hardened like salve, then mix Achilles' heel root, old yarrow and red oak bark ashes in with it, pouring in a little flyweed tea to strengthen it, so they said. And then she would add something else, she acknowledged. And what that something else was no one was ever able to find out until she died.

"The doctors round about had got interested in old Miss Zua's cures, and they came many a time to question her. But she would never tell them what the final secret was in her mixtry. She would only smile at them and say in her high voice, 'Stir about ye, men, stir about ye.'

"When she got down on her deathbed and the news spread, Dr. John invited several doctors up from Fayetteville and down from Raleigh, and they gathered there in her little shack on the bank of the creek. I heard about the gathering and went down to see what would turn up. I was always anxious to collect any folklore I could. The doctors talked and pleaded with her to tell them what the secret ingredient was, but she lay mum as a post looking up at the ceiling and saying nothing.

"Just before she died, Aunt Lodie Blalock, the sanctified woman who was waiting on her, said Miss Zua told her she had the recipe written down and it was in a tin box somewhere in the house. She herself had seen it once upon a time. So, forgetting the dying woman on the bed, the doctors got busy ransacking the place. They stirred about all right, as you might say. All up in the loft they went, digging among the newspapers and plunder. They even brought down a little old dusty baby carriage which Miss Zua had bought long years before at a sale when she was engaged to be married, an engagement that never came to anything since her sweetheart, Bull Massingill, a sewing machine agent, ran off with a Croatan girl and on out to the Texas Panhandle.

"At last they found the tin box behind a loose stone in the chimney. They gathered around it like flies around a piece of sugar and opened it. Sure enough, they found a receipt, or recipe. Dr. John read it out loud. It told the same story of sorrel, pewter plates and Achilles' heel, old yarrow, and the rest of it. Then at the last it said that the final ingredient, and that was the secret one, was to make the patient believe in you.

"Yes, that was the secret of her success. The folks she cured believed she could cure them. Well, you might know the doctors were a lot of disappointed fellows, for that part of the cure was outside their science. They all turned back to the bed to argue with the old woman, saying there must be something else. But there she was lying dead as a wedge with a smile on her lips. One of the young doctors spoke up quick-like and said, 'Look at her smiling. Just like she was glad to have fooled us.'

" 'Yes she did, she fooled us,' said another.

" 'I wonder if she did after all,' said Dr. John, who was wise in experience and years.

"A young doctor at Duke University to whom I told this story said Miss Zua's herbs might very well have cured skin cancer but not the real carcinoma. 'A cure for that dread killer still remains to be found,' he said, 'and it will be.'

"Then he asked me if I smoked cigarettes. 'A little,' I said. 'Then you better quit it,' he said. 'It's my firm belief that cigarette smoking helps cause lung cancer.' Later I did quit. This young doctor was a real pioneer, as time has proved, and I regret I don't have his name."

PLANK ROADS

SOME YEARS BEFORE THE CIVIL WAR and while longleaf pine forests were thick and plentiful, the plank road craze struck our state. The then thriving Valley town of Fayetteville was the center of it. The best known of these roads were the Fayetteville and Western and the Fayetteville and Albemarle. The state invested some $180,000 in them and, according to Lefler and Newsome in their *History of North Carolina*, received a total of $37,450 in dividends. Some eighty-four companies were chartered in North Carolina in the 1840's and 1850's, but only about a dozen roads were built, they report. The most important one stretched 129 miles from Fayetteville through High Point and Salem to Bethania in Forsyth County. This was the longest ever built anywhere. These roads cost about $1,500 a mile—about one-tenth as expensive as railroads.

At that time the supply of longleaf pine timber seemed inexhaustible, and the sawmills in the Valley were kept busy supplying the road needs. Heavy timbers were laid down and the planks—some eight to ten inches wide and two inches thick—were placed across them and close together with big nails.

"Turnouts" were provided at proper intervals for vehicle-passing. Tolls were collected at tollgates at the rate of half a cent a mile for a man on horseback, one cent for a one-horse team and two cents for a two-horse team.

The roads prospered for a few years but, as the builders must have known, the planks soon rotted and had to be replaced. It was a losing proposition, and by 1860 most of the roads were out of use. The Honorable John A. Oates in his voluminous *The Story of Fayetteville* quotes from an overseer's letter of the times as to labor costs. "Two-horse teams were paid $1.50 per day for hauling and laborers 50 cents per day or less. Numbers had to be sent away that came to hunt for work."

RAIL FENCE

THE ZIGZAG FENCE made from split rails and in the old days common throughout the Valley. They were called snake fences, sometimes worm fences, because of their shape.

The farms, when I was a child, were fenced in and the hogs and cattle ran loose to eat acorns and graze in the reeds in the swamps. These rails were split usually from ten-foot lengths of longleaf pine logs, and the fence was from nine to ten rails high, up about as high as a man's shoulders. Bottom fence rails were chosen for their solid heart and long lasting against rot. Men used to measure their strength by bragging about how many rails they could split in a day. I remember hearing Clinton McNeill, a hard-working Negro, say once that on one day in his life he split a thousand rails.

Keeping them mended, for they were always rotting down, especially the bottom rail, was a chore I despised as a boy and young man, next to digging potatoes. Old Sid Oates, like many another farmer, got up in arms when the no-stock law was passed by the state, which said that from now on the situation was to be reversed— where before the farms were fenced in and the cattle left free, now the cattle must be fenced in and the farms left free.

"Why, my god A'mighty!" said Sid, "The gover'mint's gone slam crazy." And he got out his shotgun and threatened to shoot anybody that tried to keep his cattle from running wild. "My hogs and cows have been free to go where they wanted, so did my daddy's, so did my gran'daddy's and beyond him to the founding of this country. Yessir. A man's got his rights and liberties g'arnteed by the Constitution and now they're trying to take 'em away from him. Why, our forefathers fou't at Lexington for just that, and I'm ready to fight now."

So did old Sid and others like him in the Valley talk and threaten. But to no avail, and the juggernaut of progress rolled on over them.

PINE

John Kuners

NEGRO MUMMERS. There used to be a lot of Christmas mumming and serenading in the old days. One of the most impressive Valley customs of all was the visit of the late John Kuners. These were young Negro boys and men who went around with tatters and strips of gay colors sewn to their clothes. Some of them wore women's garb. They were disguised in all sorts of homemade masks, some representing fox faces, 'possums, hogs, Rawhead-and-Bloody-Bones, Plat-Eye and the Headless Girl, which they called Kuner faces. They would rattle cow bones and dried-out horse ribs, blow rams' horns, blow harmonicas, toot on guano bugles, and collect pennies and food from door to door. The leader often carried a long blacksnake whip which he whizzed through the air like an exploding firecracker. It used to be hard to get the children to go to bed so old Santa Claus could look after their stockings until the John Kuners had gone by singing their song about—

> *"They's misery in the mountains,*
> *They's smoke upon the hill,*
> *And they ain't no coming shuteye*
> *Till the Kuners had their fill.*
> *Hah-low,*
> *Here we go!*
> *Hah-low!"*

The custom has long ago died out, and it's a pity. For it was a fearsome and thrilling sight to see them coming up the lane in the darkness with their pine-splinter torches waving above their wild costumes and making their terrible and outlandish noises. Old men have told me they heard this custom was brought over from Africa or the West Indies with the first slaves.

The Itch

T HERE ARE ALL SORTS of folk cures for the itch. Now I remember we boys used to have a vulgar rhyme which we would recite with great glee:

> *"Old John Jones is a son of a bitch,*
> *His cod rotted out with the seven-year itch."*

And most often, of course, we would use the name of some neighbor and, behind his back and with him never knowing it, have great gales of laughter at his expense, as we imagined in our minds his terrible condition. One of the best Valley cures was the use of sulphur—burn it in one's room, and also rub it on your body. My brother John and I once caught the itch, and so we used the sulphur cure, and we nearly stifled ourselves in our little shed room and created a stink all over the place. We got well, of course. Whether the sulphur helped cure us, I don't know.

Mr. Mac tells me that the pokeweed root is the best cure there is for itch.

"Yessir," he said to me one day, "it will cure the seven-year itch and that's the toughest skin disease there is.

"Old Prentice Thornwell had the worst case of it anybody ever heard of in the Valley country. He tried everything from worm grease to 'possum-gut salve. His skin got so tender with his everlasting scratching that he could hardly lie between the sheets.

"One day Miss Hettie Crews, the maiden schoolteacher, come over to Thornwell's house to confer with him about one of his children that had misbehaved in school. She found him in a pitiful condition, setting by the fire warming himself in the cold weather and scratching away. Out of her sympathy she told him about her own mother—how once she had had a terrible skin disease and a pokeroot mixture had cured her. She told him that her mother had some of the root beat up into a pulp and mixed with hot water, and she bathed in it, and it cured her absolutely.

"Well, Prentice was ready to try anything, so no sooner said than done. He sent his wife and some of the children out and they dug up a supply of root, beat it up with a maul and put it in a barrel, the way Miss Crews told him, and filled it with warm water. Prentice had it filled in the barn and he went out there, took off his clothes, and crawled in the barrel to give himself a good soaking. Meanwhile Miss Hettie and the women folk sat around on the porch talking and fixing things about the young boy's misbehavior.

"All of a sudden a loud scream sounded from the barn, the stable door burst open and there came Prentice, naked as the day he was born, jumping and squealing and fighting at himself like a million hornets were popping their stingers in him.

"Mrs. Thornwell rushed out in the yard all aghast, same like the sky was about to fall in on her and, as Prentice tore by her, he shrieked out, 'I'm in the flames of hell, woman. Fan me, fan me!' And around the house he went and his wife after him, waving her apron in the air like shooing chickens into the coop.

"Miss Hettie fled indoors and shut herself away from the sight and the children hopped up and down in the yard laughing. Finally, Prentice could stand it no more and leaving his circling around the house, he made a beeline for the creek and he dived into the old tanning hole, cold as it was, and there he sat in the icy water up to his ears like a frog. The children later carried him some clothes down there and left him.

"About daydown he came back across the field dressed and in his right mind. He was so ashamed though that for weeks he wouldn't go to church. But it cured him all right. Yessir, the itch never bothered him the rest of his three score years and ten. In fact, his hide was so tough that he could run through a briar patch and never get scratched.

"Yessir, pokeweed root mixture will sure cure skin disease, whether it's the two-weeks kind or the seven-year itch. You try it sometime, Mr. Green, and if you want some good eating, take the tender leaves when the pokeweed is coming up early in the spring and eat it. I've eaten many a mess of it myself and I'm sure it's good for the health."

SMOOTH SUMAC, FALL COLOR

PAUL GREEN, THE WRITER

by Laurence G. Avery
President, The Paul Green Foundation

PAUL GREEN'S LIFE was so richly diverse that it is hard to characterize. Many of his most consequential activities were in the area of social justice, where beginning in the 1920s he played a leading role in abolishing chain gangs in the South and in pushing toward fairness for minorities in capital punishment cases—with the ultimate aim of abolishing that form of punishment. Long before it was popular he also advocated equal opportunities for African Americans and Native Americans, especially educational opportunities, and worked hard to break down the barriers of segregated school systems in his home state. Green was part of the core group of young people coming out of World War I whose enlightened and transformative efforts over the next several decades caused North Carolina to be viewed as the most progressive of Southern states.

At the same time Green's chief work was writing. Developing as a playwright in the folk-drama atmosphere generated by Frederick Koch at the University of North Carolina, Green came to the world's attention in 1927 with the award of the Pulitzer Prize for Drama for *In Abraham's Bosom,* a ground breaking play for its authentic depiction of African American experience in the rural South. Green went on to write other notable plays including *The House of Connelly*, which launched the Group Theatre in 1931, the anti-war musical *Johnny Johnson,* which gave the composer Kurt Weill his first opportunity to work in the American theater, and *Native Son,* which Green dramatized in collaboration with the novel's author, Richard Wright. In the early days of talkies Green went to Hollywood and wrote several acclaimed motion picture scripts, among them *Cabin in the Cotton,* which gave Bette Davis her first starring role, and *State Fair,* starring Will Rogers. Back in North Carolina in 1937 he wrote *The Lost Colony*, an outdoor historical play commemorating the earliest English settlement in the new world and its egalitarian legacy to American democracy. *The Lost Colony,* produced on Roanoke Island, site of the original settlement on the North Carolina coast, has played each summer now for well over sixty years and has inspired a nation-wide interest in outdoor plays celebrating local history.

I met Green in the 1970s and spent about a decade editing his letters, frequently working at his home, Windy Oaks, a rambling farm house a few miles out of Chapel

Hill, where most of his papers were located. The poet and fellow North Carolinian Carl Sandburg called Green "one of the best talkers in the U. S. A.,"[1] and his delightful letters, which Green saw as but another form of conversation, provide an unrivaled picture of him as a person going about his life. His personality sings through the letters as it did in daily conversation, and his many activities are there by way of comment and discussion. Green died in 1981, and in 1983 his wife and children established the Paul Green Foundation to carry on work in the areas of his abiding concerns in the arts and human rights. The Foundation supports professional productions of work by promising young playwrights and does much to encourage developments in the field of outdoor historical drama. The Foundation also endeavors to promote social justice by combating the legacy of racism and encouraging serious efforts to ameliorate capital punishment and eventually relegate it to the past. Over its history of more than twenty years, the Foundation has compiled a distinguished record.

In her Preface, Betsy Moyer explains how she took entries concerning plants from her father's *Wordbook* and used them as the text for the current work, *Paul Green's Plant Book: An Alphabet of Flowers and Folklore.* Not surprisingly, plant references are numerous in the *Wordbook* because the natural world was constantly in Green's awareness. Upset by some turn of events, for instance, he could take a walk in the woods and feel restored: "the deep, delightful woods," he mused in a letter, "warm and glowing in their autumn colors—maples, oaks, hickories, sourwood, black gum and the ever, ever present dogwoods. And then dark and enfolding over it all the great tall pines. To go there for [me] is like going to church."[2] Green was Wordsworthian in the way the physical environment registered on his emotions and imagination.

The special feature of the *Plant Book* is that with most textual entries there is a striking photograph of the plant in its natural habitat. The result is a work that is a delight to read—and to look back at any time the name of a plant native to North Carolina catches your eye. *Ah yes,* you can say, *that's what it looks like! And I had forgotten they used to make tea from its roots for the croup!*

[1] Carl Sandburg to Paul Green, 12 April 1961, Paul Green Papers, Southern Historical Collection, Wilson Library, University of North Carolina at Chapel Hill.

[2] *A Southern Life: Letters of Paul Green, 1916-1981*, ed. Laurence G. Avery, (Chapel Hill: University of North Carolina Press, 1994), p. 672.

A Profile of Paul Green

by his daughter Janet M. Green

He had a perfect name. Not only did he embody the abounding vigor associated with the ancient English name of "Green," but he loved every thing else of that potent color. He walked the fields and meadows and woods of this world, not as a stranger but as a devoted admirer and protector. "Green-growing friends of life" I called him and my mother in an anniversary poem, and so they were.

Caring for weaker things was natural to him. If you were a plant or bush, he tried to learn all your names. He might transplant you to better ground, but there he would look after you. He planted and cared for plants and trees on his own land and also saved many around his outdoor theaters from ferocious bulldozers. His cabin workplaces and his homes, Greenwood and Windy Oaks Farm, were surrounded by trees, plants and bushes.

> *"How could such sweet and wholesome hours*
> *Be reckon'd but with herbs and flowers?"*[1]

Along with such care went his desire to master the world of green. As a farmer and a farmer's son, he knew much more about this world than most people. My mother marveled that he could identify a tree in winter by its bark. He was less sure of flowers. He was determined to learn the proper Latin names of wildflowers on his Windy Oaks Farm property, and in the last years of his life transplanted many of these from the adjacent woods to the slope behind the house. He stuck little white sticks with their identifications on them to help him memorize their botanical names. He was not amused when I teased him about his "bird cemetery." Etymologies fascinated him. He had studied and continued to study Latin and Greek, and he and my mother, both students of folklore, had an abiding interest in the vivid folk names for plants and trees and their traditional uses.

His curiosity about the world was a source of his astounding energy. He was curious about everybody he met—waitresses, cab drivers, students—and this same friendly and appreciative interest extended also to the world of plants and trees. There was a sweetness in Dad's nature that seemed to say, "We are all here together."

He used the natural world to teach his children gentle moral lessons on our many walks through the woods, especially, as I recall, the age-old one that death and life are inextricably bound together—the springing shoots from the rotting stump, the odd yellowing twigs on the green tree that foretold the death of summer at summer's height.

He wasn't interested in teaching me the uses of plants and trees—no survivor lore—but he was very interested in other people's uses, as illustrated by the incredible way Indians made buckeye meal to get fish drunk. He did give much detail as a baseball pitcher about the way he anointed baseballs with slippery elm or alder juice and spit to transform them into deadly spitballs.

The stories he noted lovingly over many years were really a little history of the people who made and transmitted them. Dad was preserving their experience— their love potions, their medicines, their toys, their drinks and foods, their sayings— much as he preserved people's experience in his other writing. Many of the comments quoted in this *Plant Book* from his *Wordbook* have narrative appeal, or are little vignettes, sketched with a few words. In his observations he often characterizes himself as a boy. Thus he connects his childhood memories to the modern world through the living plant.

Though he places many of his comments in his native Harnett County, North Carolina, many of the flowers that appear in this book bloomed around Greenwood, and he probably also noted them there. Perhaps some still exist in those woods, so beloved to him, his wife, and his children.

In the spring there were dogtooth violets, spring green and gold, wild azaleas, anemones, bloodroot, wild strawberry and blackberry, hepaticas, wild ginger (those shy little folded ears peeking through the dead oak leaves), violets, bluets. There were also flowering trees and shrubs like wild cherry, dogwood, and redbud—twice lovely when they bloomed at the same time.

And in the hot North Carolina summers, asters, daisies, jewel weeds growing by the tangled, steamy creek. (Does anything surpass a summer evening with honeysuckle in bloom, a whippoorwill, and a moon?)

Yes, the woods and fields of North Carolina offered Dad rich and lasting pleasures. This book, the result of my sister Betsy's devoted labor, and graced with glorious photographs by her and my sister Byrd, brings him once more to life. I can see him now walking through the woods, clearing the path of some impediment—always making things better—talking to his companion, noting how the seasons were progressing and if the woods needed rain, observing things around him and at his feet, thus transforming everything that's made *"To a green thought in a green shade."* [2]

   [1,2]*Poetry quotes from* The Garden *by Andrew Marvell, 1621-1678*

THE FOLKLORE OF PAUL GREEN

by Dr. William Ferris, Center for the Study of the American South
University of North Carolina at Chapel Hill

PAUL GREEN'S LEGACY TOUCHES US in more ways than we can measure. Like his friend Thomas Wolfe, Green was a big man whose presence was felt when he entered a room. He was and remains an important presence for the University of North Carolina, Chapel Hill.

Growing up on a farm in rural North Carolina, Paul Green was inspired by the voices and natural beauty of his world. His home bordered the Cape Fear River which begins in Chatham County, near Chapel Hill, and flows to the Atlantic Ocean. Its waters link the two worlds, nature and the folk, that nurtured him throughout his life. Green drew heavily on those two worlds as the foundation for his career. At the same time he made a special contribution to folklore through his short stories, plays and novels that pulled the curtain aside and revealed the downtrodden, the poor, the black, their thoughts, their tales and their heritage.

The "Father of Outdoor Drama" was also the father of Betsy Green Moyer and Byrd Green Cornwell, who collaborated with his granddaughter Dorrit Green in the production of *Paul Green's Plant Book: An Alphabet of Flowers and Folklore.* Combining stunning photographs with text drawn from *Paul Green's Wordbook: An Alphabet of Reminiscence,* they celebrate Green's deep love for folklore and nature. The renewed interest and current research into herbal remedies demonstrates the significance of the herbal lore that Paul Green documents here. In the book Green reflects on the beauty and tenacity of "the weeds, the woods, the flowers, and other growing things in the Valley," and he asks himself, "Do these all…have the power to think?" His characteristically Southern conclusion—"Could be."

Paul Green's Plant Book offers the reader a sweet feast of photography and text that celebrate the worlds of folklore and nature that Green knew so well. It reveals Green's deep love for his region, a love that inspired his long, distinguished career as a writer and teacher.

BOTANICAL NOTES

by Ken Moore

SOME OF THE BOTANICAL NOTES draw attention to common names that are not in general usage today; other notes clarify taxonomic characteristics of specific plants; a few relate to general plant descriptions that may be misleading. The rich heritage of plant identification and usage handed down through the decades by folks for whom plants were a vital part of daily living is full of surprises.

1. Adder's-Tongue *(p. 1)* As Paul Green acknowledges, trout lily is the common name most often used for this beautiful early spring wildflower. It is curious that he gave preference to adder's-tongue in his *Wordbook*. Adder's-tongue here applied to the trout lily or dog tooth violet, with reddish stamens protruding from the flower, snake-tongue-like, should not be confused with the adder's-tongue ferns (*Ophioglossum* species).

2. Alumroot *(p. 2)* Calling the beautiful wild geranium an alumroot was a true puzzle for me as well as for all my associates at the North Carolina Botanical Garden who use alumroot in reference to *Heuchera americana*. Both plants, though of separate plant families, have traditionally offered the same or similar medicinal properties.

3. Be-Shame Bush *(p. 7)* This remarkable plant is not a shrub, but it does have a characteristic habit of spreading and sprawling over whatever is nearby, resulting in a low shrubby appearance.

4. Longleaf Pine *(p. 28)* The buds of longleaf pine in early spring are as beautiful as any wildflower. Pictured here centered in a cluster of the previous season's green leaves is the tight bud of the new season's leaves surrounded by concentric bands of buds of the male pollen-bearing cones. As the male buds mature they will elongate into the familiar yellow catkin-like cones casting off clouds of yellow pollen so common in the air and on surfaces everywhere in the spring.

5. Love Vine *(p. 29)* The stems that aggressively coil around other plants are generally orange or reddish in color. However, the numerous white flowers clustered close to the stems can give an overall white appearance to the vines.

6. Mountain Laurel *(p. 36)* The description of the laurel occurring on the north sides of hilly stream banks is certainly a correct observation. The notion that this typically mountain species "escaped" from the mountain regions by bird dispersal of seeds is thoughtful. The truth is that mountain laurel, often in association with other characteristic mountain species such as rhododendron and galax, does occur on isolated sites in the eastern Piedmont and the Coastal Plain. These sites are usually steep north facing river and stream bluffs where mountain plants remain as "relict communities" following continental glacial retreats thousands of years ago. During the former Ice Age the vegetation of present day eastern North Carolina was more characteristic of far northern climates. As more temperate plant species, along with animal species, migrated northward with warmer climate following the melting glaciers, isolated pockets of some of these characteristic mountain species remained on sites where the moisture and temperature regimes allowed for their survival to the present day, "relics" from former colder periods.

7. Muscadine *(p. 38)* Both the popular dark purple muscadine and the light brown scuppernong grapes are varieties of the same native species of grape found throughout most of North Carolina.

8. Peppermint *(p. 43)* Though this common mint introduced to America by the early pioneers is often called spearmint, there is another species, *Mentha spicata*, which is officially recognized as the true spearmint.

9. Pilewort *(p. 45)* Since the inconspicuous heads of tiny disc flowers are seldom noted or recognized as flowers, folks frequently consider the more obvious round fluffy seed heads to be flowers. The seeds are windborne, each tiny seed carried aloft by the attached "parachute" not unlike the larger similar seed structure of the better known dandelion.

10. Pitcher Plant *(p. 47)* The "opposing bristles" are actually lining the inner leaf surfaces. The red and yellow-petaled pitcher plant flowers, varying from species to species, are held separate from the insect trapping leaves and generally flower before the tubular leaves open to catch unsuspecting insect prey. This is an evolutionary development which assures that the pitcher plants do not capture and digest the specific insects upon which they are dependent for flower pollination. However, the leaves of the various species of pitcher plants are frequently mistaken as flowers, because the tubular leaf structures resemble the common popular wildflower, Jack-in-the-Pulpit (see page 112) which also occurs throughout the Valley region. It is a real curiosity that Jack-in-the-Pulpit, so common in the Valley, was not included in Paul Green's observations.

11. *Poison Sumac* *(p. 48)* Unfortunately the rash—sometimes quite severe, caused by human contact with the poisonous species of this genus, the ones bearing white berries—keeps most folks from admiring the beautiful smooth, winged and staghorn sumacs, which have dramatic orange and red fall color as well as attractive red berry clusters (see page 106). The seeds of the sumacs, even the poisonous species, are important wildlife food.

12. *Red Birch* *(p. 53)* Though this tree that reaches canopy size along most river banks is today commonly called river birch, one can easily understand the common name, red birch, referring to the lovely exfoliating reddish-brown bark characteristic of this species. Today it is so commonly observed as a moderate-sized urban landscape tree that it is seldom acknowledged as one of the giants of river banks and flood plains.

13. *Shagbark Hickory* *(p. 58)* The tree pictured is the southern shagbark hickory, a relatively rare species scattered in northern portions of the Valley. The common Shagbark Hickory, *Carya ovata*, is more frequently encountered. The two are similar in appearance to the untrained eye.

14. *Spanish Moss* *(p. 63)* This flowering plant of the bromeliad family is not a moss, though local folks refer to it as such. Seldom noticed are the interesting tiny yellow-green flowers situated within the pendulous thread-like stems and leaves. It is not parasitic, though in very warm and humid lowland regions of the deep South, the plant can become so vigorous as to be infrequently a problem in masking foliage and adding significant weight to tree limbs.

15. *Spicebush* *(p. 63)* Decades ago Paul Green commented on the dwindling numbers of this once very common shrub of flood plains and lowlands. The decrease in populations of this important wildlife shrub, particularly for native birds and butter-flies, continues today as it is slowly being displaced by the ever-spreading invasive exotic, *Ligustrum sinense,* the Chinese privet.

16. Stinging Nettle (p. 64) The noticeable white-flowered stinging nettle of the sand-hills and sandy pine flatlands of the coastal plain should not be confused with the more common stinging wood-nettle which lacks noticeable flowers and is common in moist wooded areas from the mountains through the upper coastal plain.

17. Toad-Flax (pp. 70 and 71) The yellow species, commonly called butter-and-eggs, was introduced from Europe and is seen infrequently in the Valley. The true native toad-flax turns whole fields azure blue in the early spring.

18. Turk's-Cap Lily (p. 75) Because of the similarity in the color and shape of the individual flower, the Michaux's lily, *Lilium michauxii*, which occurs throughout the State, is frequently called Turk's-cap lily. The true Turk's-cap lily, *Lilium superbum,* occurs exclusively in the mountain region. It is notable that Michaux's lily was officially declared the State wildflower, "Carolina Lily," by the North Carolina Legislature in 2003. Though occurring throughout the State, this beautiful lily is illusive, being seen only here and there, as described by Paul Green, "a spot of gold shining low in a little opening." It will be a very special moment whenever one is fortunate enough to happen upon the Carolina lily flowering in mid-summer.

19. Wake-Robin (p. 79) What is generally called wake-Robin is *Trillium erectum,* a species of the North Carolina mountains, but as Paul Green's description indicates, common names for trilliums are many. The one most likely observed in the upper Valley region and the Chapel Hill environs is *Trillium cuneatum,* and it is easy enough here, viewing the visual image, to prefer the name Daffydown Dilly.

20. White Alder (p. 81) Paul Green seems to have been relying on the Jacobs and Burlage *Index of Plants of North Carolina* for this common name. Sweet pepperbush is more commonly used. Perhaps in earlier days it was called white alder because, like the tag alder, it is common along pond edges, but, unlike the tag alder, it has very noticeable white flowers.

21. Wild Onion (p. 84) The traditional strong-flavored ramps, for which the North Carolina mountains are famous, does not occur in the Valley, but it is not difficult to imagine that the local folk may have referred to any of the wild onions as ramps.

FURTHER READING

The Flora of the Carolinas, Virginia, and Georgia,
a Working Draft of March 17, 2004, by Dr. Alan S. Weakley.

Index of Plants of North Carolina with Reputed Medicinal Uses
by Marion Lee Jacobs and Henry M. Burlage (Privately printed, 1958)

The Manual of the Vascular Flora of the Carolinas
by Albert E. Radford, Harry E. Ahles and C. Ritchie Bell
(Chapel Hill: University of North Carolina Press, 1964 and 1968)

The Natural Gardens of North Carolina by B. W. Wells
(Chapel Hill: University of North Carolina Press, 1932, revised 2002)

Paul Green's Wordbook: An Alphabet of Reminiscence by Paul Green,
Edited by Rhoda Wynn (Boone, NC, Appalachian Consortium Press, 1990)
Available from the Paul Green Foundation, PO Box 2624,
Chapel Hill, NC 27515

The Wild Flowers of North Carolina, Second Edition
by William S. Justice, C. Ritchie Bell, and Anne H. Lindsey
(Chapel Hill: University of North Carolina Press, 2005)

PHOTO: REDBUD FLOWERS

PLANT INDEX

Entries in bold letters are main entries in the body of the *Plant Book* text.

Entries in italics are botanical names.   **Page numbers in bold** refer to photographs.

Dionaea muscipula, **76**
Diospyros virginiana, **44**
dodder, **29**
dog daisy, **86**
Dog Fennel, 18
dog grass, **85**
dogtooth violet, **1**, 113
Dogwood, xx, 15, 18, **19**, 39, 57, 97

earth apple, **3**
Echium vulgare, 78
elder, **2**
Elderberry, ii, 20
ellum, 59
elm, 59
Epigaea repens, **72**
Erechtites hieracifolia, **45**
Erigeron annuus, **20**
Erythronium americanum, **1**
Euonymus americanus, **65**
Eupatorium capillifolium, **18**
Eupatorium perfoliatum, **10**
everlasting, **52**

Fagus grandifolia, **6**
false gromwell, **27**
featherweed, **52**
fever bush, **63**
field dodder, **29**
field pine, **28**
fireweed, **45**
fish-mouth, **75**
Fleabane, 20
flowering ash, **21**
flowering dogwood, 18
fly killer, **83**
flytrap, **76**
forget-me-not family, 27
Fragaria virginiana, **84**
Fringe Tree, 21
fussy gussy, **52**

galax, 114
Galium aparine, **6**

gall weed, 1
Gaultheria procumbens, xvi
Gelsemium sempervirens, **87**
Gentiana quinquefolia, 1
Geranium maculatum, **2**
gill-o'er-the-ground, **17**
Glecoma hederacea, **17**
Gnaphalium obtusifolium, **52**
Goldenrod, 21
Goodyera pubescens, 53
green and gold, **64**
groot, 79
ground cedar, **55**
ground holly, **47**
ground laurel, **72**
ground lily, **79**

hackberry, **xiv**, xv, **65**
hairy ruellia, **76**
halberd-leaved violet, **77**
Hamamelis virginiana, **85**
hazel, **85**
Heal All, 22
heart-bursting-with-love, **65**
heartleaf, **82**
hearts-a-busting-with-love, **65**
Hedeoma pulegiodes, 42
Helenium autumnale, **62**
Helianthus annuus, **66**
Helianthus tuberosus, **3**
Henbit, 22
Hepatica, Cover, 23
Hepatica americana, **23**
herb of grace, **55**
Hercules' club, **71**
Heuchera americana, 113
Hexastylis arifolia, **82**
Hibiscus moscheutos, 67
Hickory, 23, 58, 96
Holly, Cover, 24, 35
Honeysuckle, 25

horsefly killer, **83**
horsefly weed, **83**
Horse Nettle, 25
Houstonia caerulea, **51**
Hypericum spp., 56

Ilex opaca, **24**
Ilex vomitoria, **86**
Impatiens capensis, **72**
Indian shamrock, **79**
Indian tobacco, **37**, 79
innocence, **51**
Ipomoea pandurata, **84**
Iris virginica, **84**

Jack-in-the-Pulpit, **112**,115
Jamestown weed, **26**
Jerusalem artichoke, **3**
Jerusalem Oak, 26
jewel weed, **72**
Jimson Weed, Cover, 2, 13, **26**, 27, 37
Job's Tears, 27
Johnson grass, 2
Judas tree, 53
Juglans nigra, **80**

Kalmia angustifolia, **59**
Kalmia latifolia, **36**

Lady Slipper, 27
Lady's slipper, **27**
Lamium amplexicaule, **22**
lemon balm, **6**
Lepidium virginicum, **43**
Leptoloma cognatum, **85**
life everlasting, **52**
Ligustrum sinense, 115
Lilium michauxii, **75**, 116
Lilium superbum, 116
Linaria spp., 70
Lindera benzoin, **63**
Liquidambar styraciflua, **68**
Liriodendron tulipifera, **74**
little pigs, 82, **83**
live oak, **63**
liverwort, **23**

Lobelia inflata, 79
Loblolly Pine, 25, **28**, 46
Longleaf Pine, Cover, 28, **29**, **46**, 101, 102, 113
long-needled pine, **28**
long straw pine, **28**
Lonicera japonica, **25**
love-in-winter, **40**, **47**
Love Vine, 29, 113
Lycopodium flabelliforme, **55**
Lyonia mariana, 64
Lyre-leaved Sage, 30

Magnolia, Cover, 25, **30**, **31**
Magnolia grandiflora, 30
Magnolia virginiana, **67**
Maiden's Blushes, 32
mandrake, **33**
marsh mallow, **67**
Marsh Pink, 32
May Apple, 33
Maypop, 41
Meadow Beauty, 33
Meadow Parsnip, 34
Meadow Rue, vii, 34
Melia azedarach, **15**
Mentha piperita, **43**
Mentha spicata, 114
Mexican mulberry, **71**
Mexican tea, 26
Michaux's lily, 116
Milkweed, 34
mint family, 6
Mistletoe, 35
Mitchella repens, xvi, **40**
moccasin flower, **27**
Monarda didyma, 6
Monkshood, 36
Morus alba, 81
Morus spp. **37**
Mountain Laurel, 36, 114
Mulberry, 37
Mullein, 3, 37
Muscadine, 38, 57, 114
Myrica cerifera, **5**

ACKNOWLEDGEMENTS

I want to thank, first of all, my family, my husband Bill for his enduring patience and counsel, my sister Byrd Green Cornwell who contributed many fine photographs to the *Plant Book,* my sister Janet Green who wrote the lovely profile of our dad, and my brother Paul and his wife Dorrit who made a generous donation. My niece Dorrit Green has contributed the extraordinary layout and graphic design and has done much to make the book readable, enjoyable, and beautiful. And not least, thanks to Eleanor Sofia Marie Green, great granddaughter of Paul and Elizabeth Green, and her parents Paul and Catherine for tolerating the persistence of this photographer.

Especially I am indebted to Charles and Betty Cheek whose timely and generous grant through the Community Foundation of Greensboro's Prickett Fund made the *Plant Book* possible.

Many have contributed with dedication and skill—Mark Doyle and Donna Dufault of Autumn Color, Rick Marment and Mike Lee of CS Graphics, Rose Raduziner, Amy Jo Wood, Deborah Bryant, Jeaneane Williams, Lois Mendenhall. Doreen O'Connor and Johnny Randall have added beautiful images. Dr. C. Ritchie Bell, Dr. Anne Lindsey, Dr. William Friday, Richard Adler, Dr. William Ferris, and John Ehle wrote gratifying words of endorsement. Appreciation is also extended to Julie Moore and Kathleen Buck for their valuable assistance.

Early supporters of the *Plant Book* were Marsha Warren, Rhoda Wynn, and Laurence Avery, David Perry, Linda Lacy, Jackie Green, Mary Best and photography mentors Steve Maka, Budd Titlow, and John Wawrzonek. My good friends the Sudbury Valley Nature Photographers gave gentle and helpful advice.

I want to thank the Paul Green Foundation for permission to quote from Paul Green's writings and for supporting the marketing of the *Plant Book.* Also I am grateful to an anonymous donor who contributed generously through the Triangle Community Foundation.

I am deeply grateful to Charlotte Jones-Roe, Janie Bryan, Chris Liloia, Sally Heiney, Stephen Keith, Dr. Alan Weakley and the entire staff of the North Carolina Botanical Garden who opened their doors to me and showed me the way to the bloodroot. Dot Wilbur-Brooks led me to Ken Moore, who has been my collaborator, steady support, and extraordinary friend in putting this book together. To the Botanical Garden Foundation and its director Peter White, who agreed to publish the *Plant Book,* I owe the book itself.

"When you come this way again
we must go out and
walk among these trees..."

—FROM A LETTER WRITTEN BY PAUL GREEN
TO HIS DAUGHTER BETSY

Photo Credits